Mountains of Europe

MANAGING EDITORS
Amy Bauman
Barbara J. Behm

CONTENT EDITORS
Amanda Barrickman
James I. Clark
Patricia Lantier
Charles P. Milne, Jr.
Katherine C. Noonan
Christine Snyder
Gary Turbak
William M. Vogt
Denise A. Wenger
Harold L. Willis
John Wolf

ASSISTANT EDITORS
Ann Angel
Michelle Dambeck
Barbara Murray
Renee Prink
Andrea J. Schneider

INDEXER
James I. Clark

ART/PRODUCTION
Suzanne Beck, Art Director
Andrew Rupniewski, Production Manager
Eileen Rickey, Typesetter

Library of Congress Number: 88-18365

Library of Congress Cataloging-in-Publication Data

Luciana Bottoni, Luciana.
    [Montagne d'Europa. English]
    Mountains of Europe / Luciana Bottoni
    — (World nature encyclopedia)
    Translation of: Montagne d'Europa.
    Includes index.
    Summary: Describes the geographical features, climate,
and plants and animals of the European mountains with
emphasis on their interrelationship.
    1. Mountain ecology—Europe—Juvenile literature.
2. Biotic communities—Europe—Juvenile literature.
[1. Mountain ecology—Europe. 2. Biotic communities—
Europe.] I. Bottoni, Luciana, 1952-.
II. Title. III. Series: Natura nel mondo. English.
QH135.M6613 1988 574.5′264′094—dc19   88-18365
ISBN 0-8172-3325-3

WORLD NATURE ENCYCLOPEDIA

Mountains of Europe

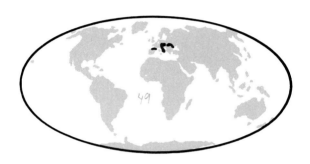

Luciana Bottoni
Lorenzo Fornasari
Renato Massa
Mia Shubert

RAINTREE PUBLISHERS
Milwaukee

CONTENTS

INTRODUCTION

Tall and towering, today's major European mountains gleam with rocks and sparkle with snow and ice. They are one of the last places where nature is not spoiled. Most of the world is becoming more and more crowded and used for farming, cities, and industry. For thousands of years people did not enter these wild mountain regions very much. It is hard to grow crops, build roads or paths, or even live in such unfriendly places. The few things that nature provides must be used very carefully by humans. Different types of human civilizations or cultures have developed over hundreds of years in Europe's mountains. These cultures depend more on their environment than cultures do in other places.

Although forests have been "tamed" by forestry, wise

management has allowed many large mammals and birds to survive. Human activities at these higher altitudes have not changed the landscape as much as in other regions. The result is better preservation of the natural environment. Today, there are still glaciers and mountainsides covered by scree, or broken rock. Areas of moraine (material moved and left behind by glaciers) are just the same today as they were thousands of years ago.

The mountains of Europe today offer the richest and most easily reached store of natural treasures, landscapes, plants, and wildlife. They are the continent's most valuable natural environment. To venture up and into these wide worlds of solitude, space, and silence is an important stage in the long journey in search of nature.

THE ORIGINS OF MOUNTAINS

Many people think that the earth has always been just as it is today. When seeing a mighty mountain range, it is hard to imagine the powerful events that formed it many millions of years ago. It is just as difficult to understand the events which are even now slowly but constantly changing the appearance of mountains.

The different major events that help to form mountain chains are collectively called "orogenesis." This process happens in a variety of stages. There is changing of rocks caused by folding and splitting from pressure deep inside the earth. This is called "deformation." Changes also occur in the structure of rocks, called "metamorphism," and there is movement of melted rock coming from deep within the earth toward the surface.

Plate Tectonics

Geologists have worked out various principles and ideas (theories) to explain the processes of orogenesis. Since the 1950s, an exciting new idea has taken root. This is the theory of plate tectonics.

According to this theory, the outermost part of the earth, called the "lithosphere," is a huge, broken sheet. The lithosphere is composed of rock similar to that exposed at the surface of the earth. It is split up into a number of huge, slightly flexible plates. These enormous plates "float" on the deep, melted part of the planet. They constantly move separately from one another.

There are three kinds of boundaries, or edges, to these plates. One boundary lies along the oceanic ridges. These are extremely long underwater mountain ranges. Magma, which is melted, fluid rock, comes to the surface along the ridges. As the magma is forced out, it increases the size of the plates. The second type of boundary is found at the edges of the continents. It is here that one plate slips beneath another as they move. The third and last type includes fractures where slippage and sideways creeping of the plates occur.

There are a variety of geological features where plates meet. These lead to the formation of different types of sedimentary, igneous, and metamorphic rocks. Sedimentary rocks are formed from various types of sediment (deposits). Igneous rocks are formed by the hardening of magma. Metamorphic rocks are formed by changes occurring to the rock structure. The study of these rocks through the ages provides an explanation of the stages through which a mountain chain goes in its geological development.

Preceding pages: Pictured is a view of the Pennine Alps from Gran Paradiso National Park in Italy. *From left to right* are the last peaks of the Giant's Tooth in the Mont Blanc group, the Grandes Jourasses, the Col Ferret, the Dent Blanche, the Dent d'Hérens, the Matterhorn, the Breithorn, the Lyskamm, and the Monte Rosa group of mountains.

Opposite page: Shown is the Pradidali pinnacle at 9,155 feet (2,791 meters) in the Alps. The dolomite rocks were formed during the Mesozoic era of geology by deposits of shells and skeletons of calcareous (calcium-containing) organisms. Magnesium salts were added later. Also, these rocks were sometimes formed by chemicals such as calcium and magnesium carbonates being carried directly into the sea. In this case, no material from living organisms was involved.

9

Stages in the long process that changes a geosyncline trench into a mountain chain are pictured. In the top illustration, the sediments deposited since the birth of the geosyncline have not yet undergone geological change. In the second illustration, the compressed sediment is starting to change shape. At the same time, the center is being pushed downward. Here it will encounter heat and pressure which will change it by metamorphism. In the third drawing, the process continues, and the new folds start to appear along the trench. In the bottom drawing, the downward movement is followed by an upward push. The mountain chain then takes shape.

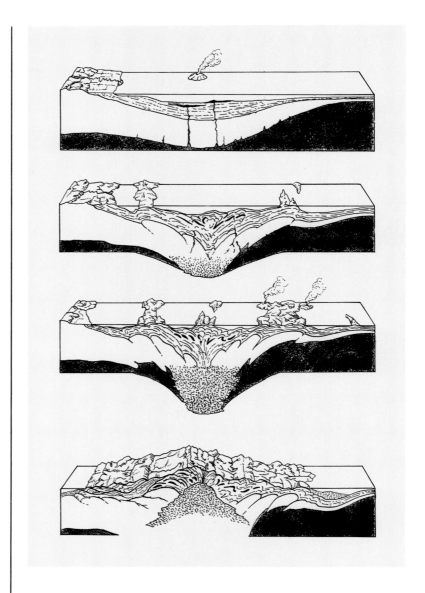

The Stages Of Mountain Formation

The first stage in the creation of mountains is the deposit of sediments in an ocean basin. Under the weight of the materials, the basin slowly sinks. The amount of material being deposited then increases because the basin is larger. The most favorable spot for depositing sediments in the seas is usually along the edges of continents. Areas where sediment is deposited are called "geosynclines."

The next stage in the birth of mountains is the formation of a trench where compression can occur. These com-

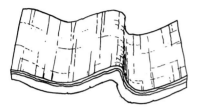

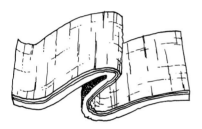

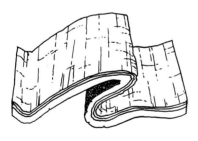

From top to bottom: Pictured is the formation of a fold in the earth's crust. When an area of the earth's crust undergoes pressure from an angle, either a fault or a fold may result. A fault is a splitting of a rock mass and movement of one part along the split. The harder a rock is, the easier it will split up into bits. A softer type of rock will fold more easily. This will happen especially if there is flexible material like marl (crumbly rock) or clay between one layer and the next. The marl or clay will act as a lubricant. This will allow the rock layers to slip past one another.

pressions cause the folding and lifting of deposits in the geosynclines. Gradually these folds become higher and higher, changing shape and shifting as they go. In this way, over millions of years, a new mountain chain is born. These events are always accompanied by volcanic activity, showing that the earth's crust is changing. Volcanoes also often form groups of islands.

Some mountain chains, like the Alps and the Himalayas, have had more complicated changes. This is because they lie close to the edges of two continents which slowly approached each other and finally collided according to the theory of plate tectonics. In such cases, there are two geosynclines, one belonging to each plate. The result is a wrinkled chain of folded mountains which piles up from movement of the earth's crust in opposite directions.

From the very moment when a mountain range emerges from the sea, the forces of wind, sun, and rain begin to tear it down. Changing hot and cold temperatures and erosion by glaciers also help to shape and mold the exposed rock.

An Example: The Alps

This basic knowledge helps to explain how the Alps were formed. The Alps are, geologically speaking, fairly young. Their shape comes from movements that happened in the Cenozoic era of geological time up to 65 million years ago. But there are traces of an even earlier history. The oldest rock formations date back to the Paleozoic era, 230 to 600 million years ago. They form the foundation of the present-day Alpine chain. This is the deep base rock of metamorphic and igneous layers on top of which more recent formations developed. During its creation, this foundation went through violent changes caused by active upward pushes.

After this stage of mountain-forming activity, the chain then eroded until the formation of a wide and level plateau (a high, flat area) was formed.

At the beginning of the next period, the Mesozoic era (65 to 230 million years ago), the crust of this plateau split. The continent of Eurasia was separated from Africa. The crack between these continents was filled by the Thethys Sea, which is today called the Mediterranean Sea. Mediterranean means "between lands." A ridge formed in the middle of this sea and began to expand. Little by little, the basin became more like a deep sea environment, and a huge geosyncline was formed.

During the later Cretaceous period, the formation of the ridge stopped and the sides of the basin began to draw closer together. In this stage, the crust of the northern plate moved beneath the crust of the southern plate. Finally the northern plate reached great depths, where it gradually remelted. At this time, there were the first violent upheavals of alpine mountain formation. Also, there were earthquakes and volcanic activity. This caused extreme folding and the first appearance of large chunks of dry land. During these upheavals, the crust, which was at first about 600 miles (960 kilometers) wide, became compressed until it was less than 60 miles (96 km) wide.

The Alps today are the folded and changed remains of geological formations which began in very different environments. Together, these remains are the evidence of a great event—the collision between two continents.

Rocks

The events described earlier show that wherever a mountain range has developed, the rocks which form the surface of the planet are uncovered. They are arranged in "formations" (distinct layers or types) of different sorts, and this makes them easier to observe. Depending on their

The entire structure of this mountain in the Dauphiné region of France consists of a huge fold tipped onto its side. It has been exposed through the erosion of the covering layer by sun, wind, and rain.

A series of rock layers called "strata," which have tilted to a slanted angle, is pictured below. The layerlike structure of rocks is the result of repeat deposits of sediment. In these processes, there may also be alternating layers of different materials on top of each other.

origin, these rocks may be classified as sedimentary, igneous, or metamorphic.

The sedimentary rocks come from a complicated chain of events. Atmospheric factors such as water and ice often work together to wear and erode rocks. This produces a mass of rubble called "detritus." This material is moved to lower areas by wind, rain, glaciers, and the force of gravity. The detritus is finally deposited on valley bottoms, on lowlands, and most often in the sea. Here it forms a sediment. In many cases, this sediment includes the remains of living organisms. When the sediment turns to rock, these remains of life are called "fossils." From them, important information about the origin and age of the rock itself can be found.

Immediately after being deposited, a sediment is unsettled and loosely packed. As new layers accumulate, the older and deeper formations are compressed. They become less porous, and, by a process known as "compaction," new rocks are gradually formed.

Sediments and rocks are constantly acted on by water,

Shown is a hardened flow of basalt by the sea in northern Europe. When it cools, basalt splits into sharp-edged pieces. As the rocks erode, they become rounded as shown by the the rocks in the foreground.

which fills even the tiniest holes. All rocks are somewhat porous. Water finds its way inside the rock and dissolves some parts of it. Also, particular ions (electrically charged particles of matter) which are sometimes present increase this dissolving power. Sometimes major chemical changes occur. After being squeezed or compacted by the pressure of the layers above, the sediment undergoes a process called "cementation." Crystals of mineral cement the sediment together. This turns it into solid rock.

The igneous rocks, also called "magmatic" or "eruptive" rocks, are formed when melted rock hardens. These rocks have a complex make-up. They form beneath the earth's crust and are called "magmas." These magmas can solidify by cooling slowly in cavities within the earth. This produces what are called "intrusive" rocks. Intrusive rocks are those which are forced into other rock masses. This

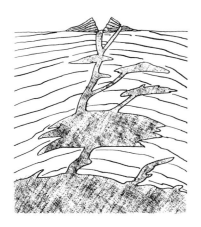

Magmas form plutonic igneous rocks when they cool and harden deep in the earth's crust. When the melted magma forces its way between other rock formations, it forms an intrusion.

solidifying process involves high pressure and large amounts of elements which are volatile (lost in the form of vapor or gas). These rocks have a highly crystalline structure.

At other times, when magmas move into already existing cracks, they may spill over onto the surface in the form of lava. When these magmas solidify, they form "extrusive" igneous rocks. These types of rocks are formed by lava which flows rather than explodes from a volcano. The cooling and drop in pressure are sudden, and there is a loss of those parts of the lava which are volatile and vaporize into the air.

A further classification of the igneous rocks is based on differing amounts of silica (chemically called SiO_2). The term "acid rocks" is used to define those in which silica is more abundant and "basic rocks" for those in which it is present in smaller amounts. It is interesting to see what happens when an "acid" magma solidifies. If the cooling is slow, a crystalline rock forms, containing quartz, feldspar, and mica. It is called "granite." Granite forms within the earth's crust. But if an acid magma cools more rapidly close to the surface, it forms a rock which is only partly crystalline, called "quartz-bearing porphyry." When there is a rapid flow of magma to the surface, the rock that forms is vitreous, or glassy. This rock is called "obsidian." It has no crystals.

In conditions where magma has been forced into cracks, a basic magma forms a crystalline rock called "gabbro." But when the magma pours out of the earth, it forms types of basalt. In these rocks, once again, the rapid cooling has not allowed minerals to form into crystals.

The metamorphic rocks result from changes in previously existing rocks. These changes may occur deep in the earth, where high temperature and pressure form an environment where the materials can remelt.

A classification of the metamorphic rocks must consider the type of rock from which they were made. The type may have been sedimentary, igneous, or already metamorphic. The classification must also consider the amount and type of metamorphism (change) made in the rock. In fact, the end result of a metamorphic process on the same type of rock can vary with different conditions of heat, pressure, and chemicals.

15

THE CHANGING SHAPES OF MOUNTAINS

When mountain chains take shape, they all share one common process. It is called "degradation," which means wearing down by erosion. It results in landslides, where material is carried downward by gravity, and in scree (broken pieces of rock). This process of erosion actually starts from the very moment when the mountain range is formed.

The main force behind erosion is water, including ice. Another factor that contributes to erosion is the result of temperature changes on rocks. These changes occur every day through all the seasons. The shrinking and expansion of the rock from temperature changes causes a network of thin cracks. Water works its way into these, gradually causing pieces to fall away from the rock. If freezing happens, strong pressure more easily breaks up the rock. This is because water expands when it changes to ice. Also, slow but steady chemical processes continually cause parts of rock to dissolve.

It is not easy to explain the shapes of mountains because the processes of erosion are complex. One example is the erosion caused by water in a valley.

Water

In the first stage of forming a valley, a stream or small river makes a path working its way deeper into the earth. At the same time, pieces of rock tumble down from the steep sides of the valley to the bottom. This process happens faster if the sides of the valley are steep. It also happens faster if the water flows rapidly. The material being carried by the water also causes an abrasive or scraping action on whatever it touches. Fast-flowing water can cut through a sandy bed, but only by carrying pebbles along with it can water cut a path through hard rock. The typical river valley undergoing erosion has a V-shape because the river erodes downward rapidly.

But a stream cannot produce this downward erosion along its entire path. In fact, when the riverbed reaches an area which is not as steep, the eroded material is then deposited at certain places. As the material left by the river starts to pile up, the level of the riverbed begins to rise. The result of this process is a very gently sloping plain. The Po Valley in Italy is a good example of this, as is the land bordering the Mississippi River. A river flowing through this type of alluvial (stream-built) plain develops a meandering path with many curves and loops.

Opposite page: Pictured is a waterfall on the Lasa River in the Stelvio National Park in the central Alps. Waterfalls are typical of an early stage in the erosion process. At this stage, the path of the riverbed has still not leveled out.

17

Pictured above is a glacial cirque lake, shaped like a steep-sided bowl, in the Gran Paradiso Range in the Orco Valley in Italy. This basin formed during the Quaternary period of geological time, extending as far back as two million years. It was made when an enormous glacier moved along a side gorge and then crossed over a ridge of metamorphic rock. In some cirque lakes, it is still possible to find glacier remains. The glacial lakes found in valleys are different from the cirque lakes. They formed from the deep excavation of an area at the end of a valley by the lower parts of glaciers, called "tongues," which no longer exist today. Examples of this are the large foothill lakes like Lake Maggiore, Lake Garda, and Lake Como in Italy.

Another typical example of the building work carried out by a stream is the delta that forms at the mouth of some rivers. This happens when the speed of the water current becomes much slower. Then the smaller particles carried in the water, like clay and mud, are deposited as sediment. Good examples of this are where the Rhine River enters Lake Constance in Austria, and where the Rhone River enters Lake Geneva in Switzerland. The delta at the mouth of the Mississippi River is well known.

Ice

Ice is also an important factor in forming a mountain range. The movement of glaciers is slow and constant. It leaves a very distinct mark on the landscape. Places where

Above: These diagrams show a V-valley *(top)* and a U-valley *(bottom).* The first valley type is caused by river erosion. The second is the result of glacial erosion.

Below: These drawings show the stages in the formation of a U-valley from an already existing river valley. *From left to right:* In the first drawing is the old river valley; in the second is the complete change in shape of the valley bottom by the glacier which has invaded it; in the third, is the typical U-shaped valley, which remains after the glacier has retreated.

glaciers have covered a large area in the past are easy to find. Glacier valleys are one of the most typical results of this action. They are often found in mountain chains which contained glaciers in earlier times. The typical cross section of these valleys is U-shaped, with the bottom flat and wide and the sides steeply sloping.

The term "U-valley" is often used to describe a glacier valley, just as the term "V-valley" is used for those produced by the eroding activity of a river.

The sides and the bottom of a glacier valley often show deep cuts and bandlike markings formed by the scraping action and erosion caused by ice. After the ice has done its work, it leaves rounded and smooth shapes, or sometimes cracks or cuts running in the direction of the slow movement of the ice. The action of ice at this point may combine with various other forces such as wind, rain, and temperature changes. Another typical result of ice is the movement of large amounts of material which are later left behind. These deposits have unusual shapes and compositions. These abandoned materials are called "moraines." They have a typical make-up which is totally haphazard and mixed. There are huge single jagged rocks, boulders, and stones, along with very fine gravel and sand. These materials have no order or layers. The large stones often show signs of being rolled along by the glacier, such as rounded, smooth surfaces.

Because of their loose composition, the moraines are more affected by erosion. Typically, they have rolling shapes with small hills and shallow low areas. There are

Above: Pictured is a spectacular view of the great Aletsch Glacier below the Egishorn summit, in the Valais canton in Switzerland. It is nearly 14 miles (22 km) long and covers 44 sq. miles (114 sq. km). The Aletsch is the largest glacier in the Alps. There are several larger glaciers in Norway, Alaska, Iceland, and Greenland.

Opposite Page: A diagram shows the drop in temperature as the altitude increases on a mountainside. The drop in temperature is more rapid at lower altitudes, about 2°F (1°C) for every 330 feet (100 m) up the mountain. Above 6,560 feet (2,000 m), this cooling rate decreases to half as much.

often blocks of rock called "erratic boulders." They are usually made of some kind of rock that is not found in the bedrock of that region.

Glacier Types

Each spring the snows melt after covering the mountains for months. There are still large areas at the highest altitudes which keep their snow all summer. This is the land of eternal ice. Although ice is always present at the highest levels of mountain ranges, it comes in a wide variety of shapes. You may notice how neighboring glaciers have different forms and reach very different levels in their journey. There is always a good reason for these differences. Glaciers are the final, visible result of permanent snow. The

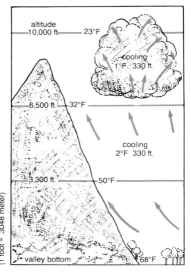

altitude
10,000 ft. — 23°F

cooling
1°F 330 ft.

6,500 ft. — 32°F

cooling
2°F 330 ft.

3,300 ft. — 50°F

valley bottom — 68°F

(1 foot = .3048 meter)

concept of the "permanent snow line" is important in understanding how glaciers form.

Since air temperature is lower at high altitudes, it is easy to understand how snowfall also increases with altitude. Above a certain altitude, snow which falls in the winter months will not melt completely in the summer. It will simply form a layer covering the snow remaining from previous years. The term "local permanent snow line" is used to indicate the altitude at which this happens.

The snow which has piled up over the years undergoes a gradual change. First it changes into granular snow, then into hard ice. The air which it used to contain gradually disappears. This change is helped along by the pressure and weight of the upper layers of snow and by the running down

21

valley glacier

cirque glacier

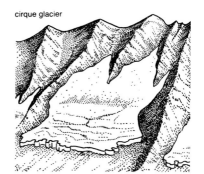

of melting surface water. Water gradually makes its way far down and replaces any remaining air. Freezing takes place in those areas that once had air.

Of course, not all mountainous areas are covered by ice above the snow line. Steep rock walls only keep a thin layer of snow. If there is heavy snow, these walls may be the location of snowslides and avalanches. But slopes which are not so steep are where snow piles up and where glaciers form. These glaciers then move slowly downhill because of gravity. The speed at which they move depends on the angle of the slope, the shape of the rocky bed beneath, and the temperature. In this way, a glacier forces its way below the snow line until the higher temperatures of these lower altitudes melt the ice.

Large caves often form at the farthest point reached by the tip, or tongue, of the glacier. Water from melted ice collects in these caves and pours out of them in strong streams.

Glaciers have shapes which are determined by the rough surface of the land. Valley glaciers, formed by an ice tongue which runs along a valley, are found typically in the alpine ranges. Upland glaciers occur in flatter areas around mountain peaks, with one or more tongues spreading out from them. They often slide down toward different valleys.

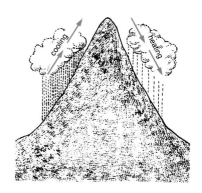

Above: When an air mass meets a mountain, it climbs up the side. While rising, it expands and cools down. At a certain altitude, the air mass cannot hold any more water vapor because it has become saturated. The water vapor then condenses, producing mist, clouds, and precipitation. Once the air has moved over the ridge or crest, it moves downward and contains less moisture. Precipitation on the other side is, therefore, lighter.

Below: A view onto a sea of clouds on the western Alps is pictured. The Bernina mountain group can be seen above it.

Piedmont glaciers are very thick and take up an entire valley until they overflow into the lowlands. Cirque glaciers, hanging glaciers, and various other types are all smaller formations without tongues. Their shapes depend on the shape of the basin in which they are found. In recent years, the growth of the glaciers on the south side of the alpine mountain chain has been reduced. Despite this, these large expanses of ice, in all shapes and sizes, still represent one of the most impressive and interesting features of the Alps.

The Mountain Climate

The high mountain regions of central Europe, named the Pyrenees, Alps, and Carpathians, have their own type of climate. This makes them distinct from the surrounding regions.

The main factors which create mountain climate are the altitude and the position of the slopes and faces of the mountains. These can be very different, even in places that are close to one another. The crisscrossing of large and small valleys, their depth, and their main direction all play a part in determining the local climate.

The two most important features of mountain climate are: 1) temperatures that are low or only average because of high altitudes, plus a more rapid loss of heat from the earth's surface because of a thinner atmosphere, and 2) winters with what are called "thermal inversions." These inversions happen because cold air is heavier than warm air and stays at lower altitudes. Lower temperatures are often found at the valley floor and warmer temperatures part way up a mountain.

The sun's rays are also stronger at higher altitudes because there is less atmosphere to act as a sunscreen. The light itself is different because it contains more ultraviolet rays. Ultraviolet light is made up of light waves that are shorter than violet light, which can be seen with the eyes. Ultraviolet light cannot be seen, but it can cause sunburned skin. Rain usually increases with altitude and is heaviest in summer and lightest in winter. Above a certain altitude, precipitation is usually in the form of snow.

EUROPE'S MOUNTAIN SYSTEMS

Europe is the lowest region in the Old World (the eastern half of the world). Its complex mountain structures show its violent geological past. The most unusual ranges are in the southern belt. Here are great, geologically "young" mountain chains rising up. The direction and the shapes of these ranges have had a great effect on the development and location of different human civilizations.

The Pyrenees

Stretching for a total of 268 miles (432 km), the Pyrenees chain has towers up between the Iberian Peninsula (where Spain and Portugal are located) in the south and France in the north. It runs from the Atlantic Ocean to the Mediterranean Sea. This is the size of the Pyrenees in visible, physical terms. But in geological terms it is actually far more extensive, since the same features are to be found in ranges located farther away.

Compared to other European mountain chains, the Pyrenees chain has some unusual features. The mountains are made up of ridges that run in a straight east-west line. The skyline is not jagged but is indented by high passes (lower areas along a mountain ridge). There are steeper slopes on the northern sides, so the valleys there are narrower. There is a gradual lowering of the mountain chain westward toward the Atlantic Ocean and a more sudden drop eastward toward the Mediterranean Sea. The peaks of the Pyrenees are not as jagged as the peaks of the Alps but are about the same height. They go from 8,530 feet (2,600 m) to 11,150 feet (3,400 m).

Like the Alps, the Pyrenees chain was also changed by the folding movements that happened in the Cenozoic era. Later these formations underwent further upward movement, forming the present-day mountain range.

Starting from the Atlantic Ocean the mountains rise up gradually. These age-old mountains stretch over smaller Cretaceous upland plateaus, formed about 100 million years ago. Here and there are deep valleys. The Atlantic Pyrenees end at the mountains called Pic d'Orthy and Pic d'Anie. In its central region, the chain is more uniform. It reaches its highest altitudes here. The peaks are made up of layers of very metamorphosed schists and limestones. Surrounding the highest peaks are signs of ancient glaciers which have carved out many small cirque lakes.

Going further east in the direction of the Mediterranean Sea, the chain has a constant, high elevation. It is cut

Opposite page: La Pierreuse, meaning "the stony one," is located in the Swiss canton of Vaud. This is a typical limestone mountain in the Alps. The geology and formation of the Alps are extremely complicated. But the mountains still have a certain type of overall "alpine" appearance.

25

A view of the Pyrenees shows the south side of the Huesca Range. The last snows still cling to the highest altitudes.

The diagram below is not drawn to scale. The height of the peaks is exaggerated. It shows the main peaks in the alpine chain and some of the most important passes. These passes have always been very important to the economy of mountain people. Passes are the routes people must take across the mountains for both business and pleasure.

through by deep, steep-sided valleys. The highest peaks surround the high plateau of Cerdagne. It was once filled with water in the late Cenozoic era. Approaching the Mediterranean Sea in the Roussillon and Ampurdan regions, the Pyrenees suddenly stop, dropping down to sea level.

The Alps

The Alps form part of an entire mountain system created by the folded formations of the Cenozoic era. These mountains reach from the Sierra Nevada in southern Spain eastward as far as Asia, ending in the Himalayas.

Compared with Europe's other mountain systems, the Alps are more impressive and have a much higher average altitude. As a result, they form a clear division between the great plains of Europe and the Mediterranean area. This is true both for the climate and geography. The areas where plants and animals live are also greatly influenced by this barrier of mountains.

Mount Blanc at 15,781 feet (4,810 m) and certain other nearby peaks over the fifteen-thousand-foot mark form the highest group in the chain. From these heights, the mountain system drops slowly downward toward its edges. Compared with other ranges which are not as high, the alpine system can be crossed at several places fairly easily. There are many passes and valleys running north-south. In recent times, many routes have been built across the Alps. These

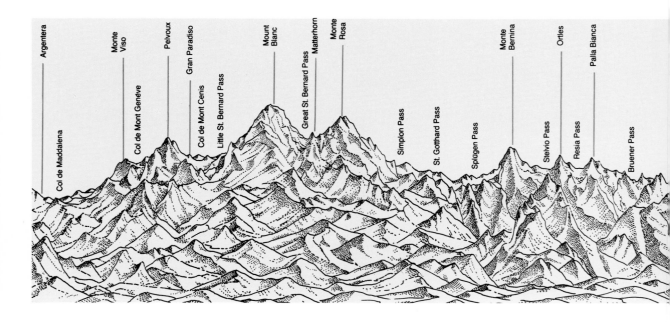

A drawing of the moraine hills is at the bottom, arranged in an arc around Lake Garda in Italy. They were left behind after the ancient Garda glacier retreated. On the slopes of Mount Baldo on the eastern shores of Lake Garda, there are still traces left by this great glacier.

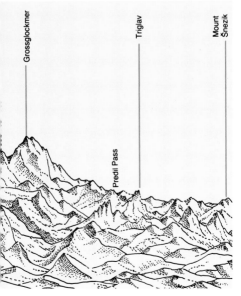

are often long tunnels which connect the various road and rail systems of the Po Valley of Italy with northern Europe.

The Alpine chain is complex in its geology and shape. Still, these mountains have a certain recognizable appearance. Geologically speaking, there are rocks of many origins. They can be igneous rocks of both intrusive and extrusive types. Or they may be sedimentary rocks of clastic, chemical, and biochemical origin. There are also porous rocks like volcanic tufa and hard crystalline rocks like schists. These different types of rocks have different resistances to erosion, especially by water. Through the ages, there have been great changes in the land's appearance. Deep gullies were carved out of the earliest rocks. These are the present-day main Alpine valleys. The sides of these valleys and the peaks towering above them still show the signs of being shaped by glaciers. In the Quaternary period,

29

these glaciers were so large and widespread that they were found right down to the lowlands. Only the very tallest peaks rose through them.

The large valley lakes, which stretch far into the Alpine mountains, clearly show the action of ice. They affect the climate of the surrounding regions, making it milder.

Even today, when changes in climate on the planet have caused glaciers to melt back to higher altitudes, it is still the glaciers which are typical of the Alpine mountain chain. This is especially so where huge ice tongues make their way downward until they meet the green forests below, as in the famous Mer de Glace, or "Sea of Ice." These glacier tongues are often split into deep crevasses and piles of seracs, which are large blocks and jagged chunks of ice.

The Apennines

The Apennine chain winds its way down the entire peninsula of Italy, forming something like a backbone. The mountains of the island of Sicily are part of this chain.

There are major differences between the Apennine landscape and the Alps. The Alps are often majestic and impressive, but the Apennines are more monotonous and uniform, at least at first glance. Still, in spite of the monotony of shapes and forms, there is great geological diversity. In the alpine chain, there is the constant presence of certain basic features. One of these is the regular arrangement of the mountains and valleys, like the folds of a paper fan. But in the Apennines, there are areas which do not have the same geological make-up or history of formation. Overall, in fact, the Apennine mountains are much more fragmented and much less uniform than the Alps.

Usually, the Apennines are divided into three main, very different sections. Each one of them has its own uniform structure and similar rock formations. The northern Apennines run from the Cadibona Pass to the Bocca Trabana. The central Apennines run from the Bocca Trabana to the Rionero saddle. Finally, the southern Apennines stretch from the Rionero saddle to the Straits of Messina.

In the northern Apennines, the rock formation consists mainly of scaly clays and clay-sand formations. This type of rock is very easily weathered. The result is a landscape with rounded shapes and wide valleys with sides often having landslides. Sometimes there are large and unexpected masses of rock emerging from the clay formations. These are either volcanic or metamorphic.

Opposite page: An autumn landscape is shown in the Emilian Apennines. In the northern Apennines, the rocks are formed mainly from scaly clays. This means that erosion by rain and wind will occur rapidly.

A summer view of the Mount Olympus Range in Greece is shown. Even in southern Europe, the highest peaks have an alpine appearance to them, both in their plant life and wildlife.

The major peaks of the northern Apennines are Mount Cimone, which stands 7,093 feet (162 m) tall, and Mount Maggiorasca, which is 5,915 feet (1,803 m) tall. One should also mention the Metalliferous Hills, rich in mineral deposits, and the short parallel chain of the Apuan Alps, which is well known for its marble.

The central Apennines are known for their high ranges. Most of the rocks are limestones and dolomites, which have harsh and rugged forms. Sometimes these central mountains show signs of ancient glaciation, such as glacial cirques, moraines, and karst formations. *Karst* refers to

regions with underground drainage, sinkholes, rolling surfaces, and caverns. This is caused by the dissolving action of water on limestone rocks.

In the southern Apennines, there are large, separated limestone peaks in the Calabrian/Lucanian Apennines and crystalline peaks in the Calabrese Apennines. Valleys and streams have cut deeply into these ranges. The Apennines of Campania show areas of volcanic activity. In fact, one of the most famous peaks is the volcano Vesuvius, which stands 4,190 feet (1,277 m) tall.

In Sicily, the Peloritani Mountains continue the Apennine chain and surround the Catania Plains with the Erei and Iblei Mountains. Soaring above the plains is the highest peak of the entire system, the active volcano of Etna which stands 10,902 feet (3,323 m).

The Carpathians

The name *Carpathians* describes the string of mountains forming an arc across central Europe from Czechoslovakia to Rumania. They cover a distance of some 800 miles (1,300 km). Their geological structure is similar to the Alps, mostly with sedimentary rocks on top of crystalline rocks. Impressive folds in this area, as in the Alps, have produced large horizontal shifts of rock masses.

Overall, however, the Carpathians are not as striking as the alpine chain. The highest peak, Mount Gerlach in the Tatry Mountains, is almost 8,860 feet (2,700 m) high, but most of the peaks do not reach the 6,560-foot mark (2,000 m). Glaciers have vanished here, since those of the Quaternary era did not reach very far. No traces of glaciers remain beyond the edge of the mountains.

The Balkans

The Balkans are a continuation of the Carpathian arc running from west to east. The ranges in the Balkan region include the mountains of Macedonia and the Rodopi Planina mountains in the south, which stretch from Bulgaria to the middle of Greece. There are also the Velebit Mountains, the Dinaric Alps, and the Albanian Alps to the northwest, running parallel to the Dalmatian coast. This last system, like the Balkans, was formed when the Alps were formed. The mountains of Macedonia and the Rodopi Range originated earlier and then experienced more change when the other mountains were being created. The mountain folds are geologically "young" and are often hit by earthquakes.

33

PLANT LIFE

The term *plant life* refers to an entire group of plants living in a certain environment or place. Plants, in other words, are not found haphazardly over the earth's surface. Rather, they occur in their own "communities." These communities, or typical groups of species, are affected by various outside factors. These include geography, climate, soil, the slope of the land, humans, and animals. There are also internal factors, connected with the plant world itself. These include relationships between fungi and plants, movements of chemicals, and the plant's own requirements for climate.

Plant communities develop until a state of balance is reached. Once this stage has been reached, there is said to be a "climax" community. Once the climax community exists, the group of plant species remains stable for a long time. This is true as long as no changes occur in one or more of the external or internal factors mentioned earlier.

There can be no single description of plant life typical to mountain chains. Plants vary with altitude and with the different climatic zones that occur from the lowest plain to the highest peak. The zones of vegetation also vary with the differing types of soils. A table of climax communities, as agreed upon by most botanists, is as follows:

1) Broadleaf forests (with trees having thick, leathery leaves)
2) Deciduous forests (trees shedding all their leaves every year)
3) Beech forests
4) Coniferous forests (trees having cones and needlelike leaves)
5) Scrublands (with bushes and small, twisted trees)
6) Alpine grasslands
7) Vegetation among rocks and rubble
8) Vegetation in tundra areas (treeless areas at very high altitudes).

Broadleaf Forests

This unmistakable forest, with its permanent foliage of tough leaves, covers large areas of the Spanish Sierras up to altitudes of about 3,300 feet (1,000 m). It also covers the foothills and lower areas of the Spanish Pyrenees, toward the two coastal ranges. In Italy, this type of forest is common. It is a typical Apennine climax community in the Mediterranean region. The main trees are holm oak, or ilex, and cork oak.

An ilex grove that has not been disturbed by people has

Opposite page: Anemones bloom in spring, with the Matterhorn in the background. The bright flowers in alpine meadows are one of the most interesting sights in Europe.

a very complex structure with different layers of trees. An upper layer, found 26 to 50 feet (8 to 15 m) above the ground, contains holm oak or ilex, false cork oak, and Japanese maple. This first layer may also have a "lower treelike layer" which is formed by strawberry trees and a shrub called "phillyrea."

Forming the next lower layer are different shrubs, mostly buckthorn and butcher's broom. Last of all is the grassy layer, which is always very small. This is because of the low amount of light coming through the tree leaves above. In fact, in many cases, this last layer has only moss or ivy like a carpet on the forest floor.

In the cork oak woods, there is an underbrush with plants similar to that of the ilex wood. Human activity has greatly changed the permanent appearance of both of these groupings of plants. One result is that cork oak woods no longer have their typical accompanying plant life.

Deciduous Forests

The deciduous forest, where trees shed their leaves, is a

In a beech forest, the undergrowth always has a thick layer of dead leaves. In this photograph, liverleaf flowers peep through the leaves.

36

typical plant grouping in central Europe. It is also present in the lower mountain zone of the ranges of southern Europe, such as the Pyrenees, the Alps, and the Apennines. This type of climax community has more oak trees than other species. In particular, there is false cork oak in the lower zone. Durmast and English, or common, oak grow in the upper zone. Here there is less moisture, which these oaks prefer.

In the false cork oak forest are various small trees and shrubs, such as hazel, hornbeam, laburnum, viburnum, and hawthorn. In the grassy layer below are liver leaf, Christmas rose, red geranium, wild asparagus, and others. In the durmast and common oak forest, on the other hand, elm, wild cherry, and lime trees can be found. The underbrush contains many plant species, with shrubs such as privet, buckthorn, and alder buckthorn. Herbaceous, or nonwoody, plants include cyclamen, bellflower, primrose, anemone, monkshood, and others.

In the Apennines, both durmast and false cork oak grow with another species of oak called "Turkey oak." This tree, however, only grows in certain places in the foothills where the climate is particularly mild. Because of human activity, the spread of oak woods in low-mountain or foothill areas has not been possible. Instead, there is the chestnut tree. In

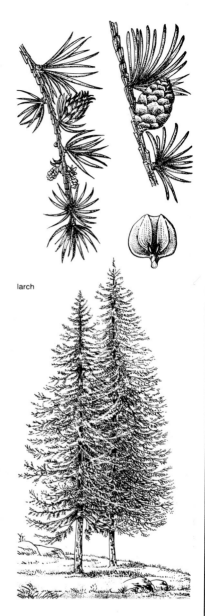

larch

The larch is a very typical alpine tree. It grows up to 8,200 feet (2,500 m), and, outside the Alps, it is found only in a few other European ranges. Above is a pair of larch trees and, at the top, the male and female flowers.

Opposite page: A beautiful larch woods is pictured. These woods allow much more light to pass through to the ground than fir woods. This is because the leaves are not very large. In the front of the picture is a cherry tree with its red autumn leaves.

the past, the chestnut tree was especially valued for its fruit. The nuts were a source of food, mainly for poorer people. This has helped the chestnut tree to become widespread. Chestnut woodland occurs only where the climate is suitable. It does not do well in low temperatures; it also avoids dry, brightly-lit environments. That is why it grows higher up on south-facing slopes, beyond the 3,280-foot mark (1,000 m). The underbrush contains mainly bracken and includes a wide variety of mushrooms and fungi.

Beech Forests

The actual mountains begin at the top of the oak and chestnut woodlands. Here there are various broadleaf species. They grow best in a cool, damp climate where there are no large changes in temperature and no long dry spells. This zone, which occurs in all of the European mountain chains, contains mainly the beech tree. This species requires medium humidity and does not like bright light or extreme cold. In the Alps, the beech tree is most common in the eastern ranges because of the type of climate it requires. In the Alpine beech forests, the shrubby underbrush contains sycamore maple, yew, heather, spurge laurel, and laburnum. In the grassy layer are blue thistle, sweet woodruff, wood lettuce, sheep's sorrel, violet, cyclamen, and bird's nest orchid. This orchid is so-called because of its many roots, twisted in the shape of a bird's nest.

The beech tree does not always form pure woodlands. In the central Alps, it may combine with silver fir, which has almost the same climatic needs. In the Apennines, beech is the most common broadleaf species. In the Alps, it is found with silver fir more often than it is found alone.

The underbrush in the Apennine beech forests includes certain species already mentioned in the alpine beech forests. It also has certain local species such as the Neapolitan cyclamen, the Apennine anemone, and the Abruzzi buttercup. Among the shrub species are the common or field maple, laburnum, and holly, especially in mixed forests with silver fir.

The use of the beech tree by humans has caused harm to many beech forests in the Apennines. They are now only clumps or groves of young trees useful for occasional cutting.

Frequent cutting has reduced the size of the trees, causing them to take on a more bushy appearance. Also, the underbrush is not as large in amount or kinds of plants as it

Right: This diagram shows how the föhn is formed. This drying wind poses no problem for the larch. It originates when an air mass loses its moisture as it rises up the side of a mountain. This air mass, which is now dry, moves on down the opposite slope. It becomes compressed (by more air pressure) and warmer. Usually the föhn blows north from the southern slopes of the Alps. Once it has crossed the mountain chain, it drops down toward the northern valleys of Switzerland and the Tyrol in Austria. Similar winds are formed in other mountain chains. These may begin near oceans and become full of humidity. When they meet a mountain chain, the moisture is then lost as the winds rise up the mountain slopes. In the Pyrenees Mountains, such a wind is called the "autan." In the Rocky Mountains, it is called the "chinook."

Scotch pine

black or Austrian pine

used to be. Despite this, it is still possible to admire some huge "natural" beech forests growing in perfect harmony with their surroundings in the central and southern Apennines.

Coniferous Forests

The lower mountains have beech trees in the lower zone and conifers in the upper. These forests can be further divided into two subzones: one with evergreen conifers (which do not shed all their leaves at once); the other with deciduous conifers. Among the conifers which form forests are Scotch pine, Norway spruce, larch, Swiss pine, and black or Austrian pine. The most obvious feature of these species is that they all have small leaves which are needle-shaped and usually remain on the branch all year round. One that does not is larch, the only deciduous or leaf-shedding conifer among the species mentioned.

In southern Europe, coniferous forests are found only in the mountains. In northern Europe, they cover mountain chains and plains. In these forests are huge and majestic trees. The most common species is Scotch pine. Because it grows in so many places, Scotch pine cannot really be called a typically alpine conifer. It can be found in most lower mountain zones, especially in the central Alps on south-facing slopes. Here the beech tree fails to find the climate it needs. These mountain slopes are dry and brightly lit, which is good for the Scotch pine's growth. Also, it can survive drying winds such as the föhn, which is typical of the local mountain climate. In the underbrush be-

Norway spruce

neath the Scotch pine are species which share its ecological (environmental) needs, such as pink heather, juniper, and common barberry.

In the eastern Alps, on the limestone and dolomite peaks, Scotch pine sometimes grows with black or Austrian pine. In natural forests, these two species grow together only in the Carnic and Julian Alps. Elsewhere, they have been planted by people to reforest other parts of the Alps, especially in the Karst region of Yugoslavia. Here they grow well on arid, stony ground. But black pine does not grow above an altitude of 4,000 feet (1,200 m), while Scotch pine is commonly found up to 6,560 feet (2,000 m).

Black pine also grows in a small area of the Abruzzi

Pictured is a Norway spruce after a heavy snowfall. Unlike larch, this conifer retains its needles throughout the winter. It can also stand low winter temperatures and spring frosts. Above are its male and female cones.

Red bilberries grow in the underbrush. People pick these and the black bilberry in large quantities. Usually the harvest is controlled by local laws and regulations. The aim of these laws is to reduce the damage done by the berry pickers. Pickers will trample young plants to reach the berries. They also use rakes which break off both fruit and small branches. The plant's reproduction is harmed when professional picking causes damage.

Apennines. But these trees seem to be a leftover from earlier times. They grow at an altitude of 3,280 to 4,430 feet (1,000 to 1,350 m) here but have disappeared from the rest of Italy. Another typical coniferous forest in the Apennines is formed by Corsican larch, which stretches from the Sila of Calabria in Italy's toe to the northeastern slopes of Etna in Sicily.

The coniferous forest in the upper mountain zone typically includes fir woods. These woods connect the alpine vegetation to the mountain vegetation of central Europe, especially in the Carpathians. Norway spruce does not grow west of the Alps and the French Massif Central. It is thus absent from the Pyrenees Mountains. In northern Europe, however, it grows as far north as Scandinavia and Russia.

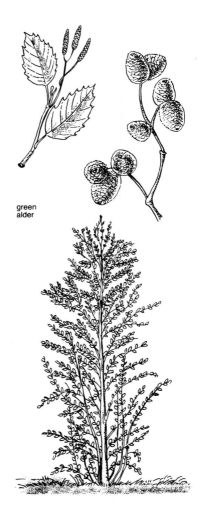

green
alder

There its area of growth meets that of the Siberian spruce, a species much like Norway spruce. In Italy, small areas of these spruce woods can be found in the northern Apennines. But discoveries of fossil pollen show that in the past it grew in other areas in central Italy. Norway spruce is a very hardy tree. Although it needs quite a bit of moisture and low average temperatures, it can survive in fairly dry conditions under bright sunlight. For these reasons, it usually grows by itself above the beech tree level.

There are many broadleaf woods which have been humanly "coniferized" by planting Norway spruce because of its highly-prized timber. The coniferization of a woods (for example, a beech woods) unfortunately causes permanent damage to this environment. In fact, the spruce forest is very thick and dark. Underneath the trees are mainly fallen needles. As these needles decay, they make the soil very acidic. It is this acidity in the ground which causes the damage. The beech tree, for example, cannot grow in soil which changes in this way.

Because of low light, there is little underbrush in the spruce forest. The main plants are bilberry of both red and black varieties, wild raspberry, sheep's sorrel, and, rarely, twinflower. Among the scattered smaller trees are rowan-tree or mountain ash. But there are many mosses, lichens, mushrooms, and fungi.

A subzone with deciduous conifers like the larch is quite different from an area having evergreen conifers but only in the continental (central) Alps. In the intermediate

Juniper "berries" are really ripe female cones. People pick them in large amounts for making aromatic alcoholic drinks and for spicing food.

This photograph shows a mixed forest of larch, fir, and beech in autumn. The dark green firs stand out from the golden yellow larch trees and reddish beech trees. Fir trees keep their leaves throughout the winter.

Swiss pine
or cembran pine

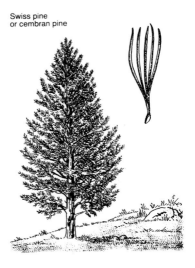

ranges and in the foothills, larch often takes over spruce forests. In these woods it is easy to identify these trees by their light green color, contrasting with the dark green leaves of Norway spruce. The larch is a very typical alpine tree. A few larch trees can be found at altitudes up to 8,200 feet (2,500 m). They grow almost entirely in the Alps themselves. Elsewhere, they grow only in a few places in the Carpathians and in Poland. In Siberia, there are other species of larch similar to alpine larch.

Unlike other mountain conifers, larch has tender, short leaves scattered in small clusters on long, slender branches. This permits the sun's rays to pass through the foliage, making these woods seem very light and airy. The loss of its

Swiss
mountain pine

leaves in autumn protects the larch against losing water
through the leaves, a process called "transpiration." During
the winter months, water cannot be absorbed through the
roots of the frozen ground. The larch is thus a tree that
stands up very well to extreme cold, sudden temperature
changes, late frosts, and dry air.

Another feature of larch is its need for a great deal of
light, which is why it forms rather sparse woods. When
animals graze among larch trees, they eat the shrubs while
all of the grass species remain. The area then becomes like a
wooded park.

The greater amount of light in the larch forest is why
there is more underbrush. In particular, there are more kinds

This diagram shows the vertical arrangement of mountain plant life. As the altitude changes, only certain kinds of plants grow together. This is because the climate is different at different altitudes. Other factors affecting where plants grow are the type of soil, wind, and the amount of sunlight.

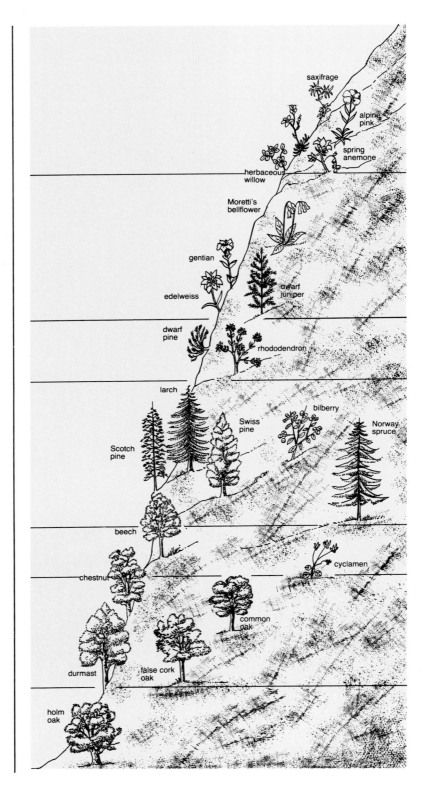

Vegetation on crags, rubble, and snow valleys

Pastures and grassland

Twisted shrubs

Conifer forest

Beech forest

Deciduous trees forest

Forest of trees with tough leaves

saxifrage

alpine pink

spring anemone

herbaceous willow

Moretti's bellflower

gentian

dwarf juniper

edelweiss

dwarf pine

rhododendron

larch

bilberry

Swiss pine

Norway spruce

Scotch pine

beech

cyclamen

chestnut

common oak

durmast

false cork oak

holm oak

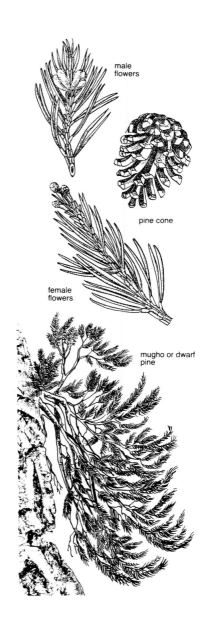

male
flowers

pine cone

female
flowers

mugho or dwarf
pine

Following page: Cattle are grazing in an Apennine meadow in southern Italy. In all the mountain regions of Europe, livestock is taken to higher pastures in the summer where the animals can enjoy rich, high quality grazing.

of shrubs. These include rhododendron, red and black bilberry, juniper, green alder, and bearberry, which is like red bilberry.

Finally, larch is important in colonizing rocky slopes or areas covered with broken rocks around the upper parts of mountain streams. It often grows with the Swiss pine, also called cembran pine. This is a short, dark green tree with sturdy branches fanning out from the trunk. Unlike larch, it does not usually grow by itself. More often it grows with larch, Norway spruce, or Swiss mountain pine. It grows in the altitude zone ranging from 5,250 feet (1,600 m) to the upper tree line. A few trees may grow up to altitudes of 8,200 feet (2,500 m).

Swiss pine came to the Alps from Siberia because of glaciation during the Quaternary period. During this time, the earth's climate was cooler, and the trees could spread to new areas. In Siberia, it forms vast forests. Elsewhere in Europe, it is only found in the Carpathian Mountains. It needs the same climate as larch. In the past, it was probably much more widespread. In many places today, people have replaced it with spruce for forestry needs. Its underbrush contains many types of plants because, like larch, it lets plenty of light through to the ground. The plants which grow in larch and spruce woods are often similar. When they differ, it is because of the type of soil. The soil may be siliceous (sandy, formed from silica) or calcareous (formed from limestone). Common plants here are rhododendron, bilberry, green alder, ling, heather, and daphne.

The last of the five major conifers found in the coniferous forest is Swiss mountain pine. In upland plateaus (high, flat areas), this unusually shaped tree is found at the bottom of its altitude range. Here, some trees are over 80 feet (25 m) high. However, on rocky slopes and flat river deposits, and at its upper growth limit, it grows very low to the ground. This helps prevent landslides and avalanches.

Scrubland

Where the larch and Swiss pine forest ends, the landscape suddenly changes. There are few trees, and they are noticeably smaller. They are replaced by small clumps and thickets of scrub and shrubs. The most common shrub is Swiss mountain pine in its flat or "prostrate" form. Some botanists call this the dwarf or mugho variety. It is found in the central Alps and the Apennines. The hook-shaped variety is common in the central-western Alps and the Pyrenees.

In the scrubland zone, this pine bends toward the ground. Its branches twist and follow close to the slopes. Only the growing tips of the branches turn upward. This type of growth is caused by environmental conditions. To survive, the plant must use as much of the heat from the ground as it can. Also, it must protect itself from winter winds and snow. Green alder and dwarf juniper also grow into small, bushy thickets.

This scrubby environment is usually made colorful by the bright pinkish red blooms of rhododendron. There are three species found here. The red variety grows in sandy soils. The hairy-leaved rhododendron and the Alpenrose variety, on the other hand, are found in limestone soil.

The heather group includes not only rhododendrons, which are common in this shrubby zone, but also bilberries, bearberry, dwarf azalea, and heather. Heather is common in the pre-alpine, or piedmont, heathland. It cannot, therefore, really be considered an alpine plant, unlike the others mentioned.

Dryas is a pioneer plant in the limestone Alps, where there is loose, shifting, broken rock. This shrub does not grow more than 4 inches (10 cm) high. It spreads itself over the ground forming a green, interlocking network of branches. This forms a peculiar steplike plant pattern called "dryas steps." At the highest altitudes, another plant, the dwarf willow, is part of a landscape similar to the arctic tundra and forms what is called "arctic moorland." It also is a low-growing plant only a few inches high.

Alpine Grasslands

Above the upper tree line are the alpine grasslands. They look like the prairies and steppes found in lower altitudes. These grasslands dominate the mountain landscape in an altitude zone ranging from 6,500 to 10,000 feet (2,000 to 3,000 m).

There is a marked difference between "grasslands," including natural grassland, and "pasturelands." Grasslands are cut and fertilized by people, but pasturelands are used directly by sheep or livestock during "summer mountain grazing."

There are many kinds of pasturelands formed by a large number of environmental factors. Most important is the type of soil. Some plants cannot grow in certain kinds of soil. This causes the formation of different communities of plants, making it impossible to completely describe all types of grasslands. Nevertheless, it is possible to briefly describe the main plant groups, including those found at low altitudes as a result of deforestation.

Oat grasslands. Progressing from lowlands to highlands at the lower altitudes of 2,300 to 2,600 feet (700 to 800 m) is the oat grassland. This plant community contains mostly the tall oat, an excellent forage plant. It usually grows beside certain large species of umbellifer plants which are shaped like umbrellas, such as wild chervil.

Also found in this community are large daisies and small red and white clover. After the first spring cutting of the tall grasses, it is clover which grows best and colors the entire meadow with its flowers. After the autumn cutting, the coloring of these pasturelands is more reddish violet because of the flowers of meadow saffron, also called "autumn crocus." The oat grassland has formed because of the deforestation of oak woods by people. It is found in clearings in deciduous woodlands.

Trisetum grasslands. Up to about 5,900 feet (1,800 m), the permanent alpine meadows are made up of different trisetum grasslands. These grasslands were formed after the cutting of beech and fir forests. Most common in this community is trisetum, a grass which has a distinctive golden color in the summer. In early spring, these open grasslands

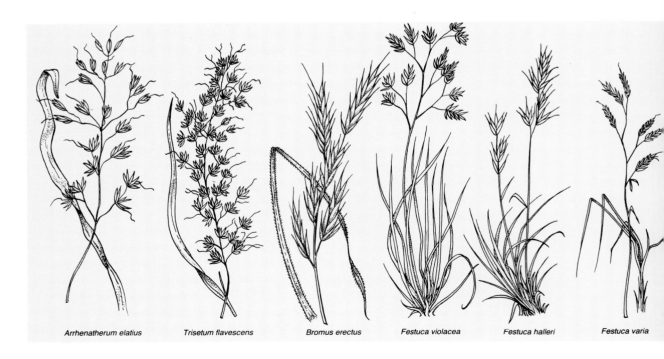

Arrhenatherum elatius   Trisetum flavescens   Bromus erectus   Festuca violacea   Festuca halleri   Festuca varia

flower with crocuses, soldanella, and narcissus. These are followed later by the flowering of daisies, bellflowers, and buttercups. Trisetum grasslands are the most stable of the various "fertile Alpine meadows" which are fertilized and cut by people.

Poa pasturelands are worthy of special mention. Poa or meadow grass is one of the most valuable forage grasses in the Alps. It grows between 4,260 and 6,560 feet (1,300 to 2,000 m). It grows in rich clay soil, well fertilized by the cattle grazing on it. The plants which grow along with poa grass are the same as for trisetum grasslands. The most common are those which like a certain amount of moisture, such as crocuses and forget-me-nots.

Brome grasslands. Upright brome, or meadow brome, is a grass which grows well in arid and exposed limestone soils. It grows in all sparse grasslands in lower mountain zones. Various types of the brome grasslands are found in arid and dry environments. Such places usually have not only upright brome grass but also fescue grasses, especially sheep's fescue, crabgrass, meadow sage, globularia, and rockrose. In more humid areas, the brome grasslands grow taller and thicker. They are the home of wild orchids and buttercups. Together with the brome grasslands, there are valley fescue meadows in the valleys of the central Alps.

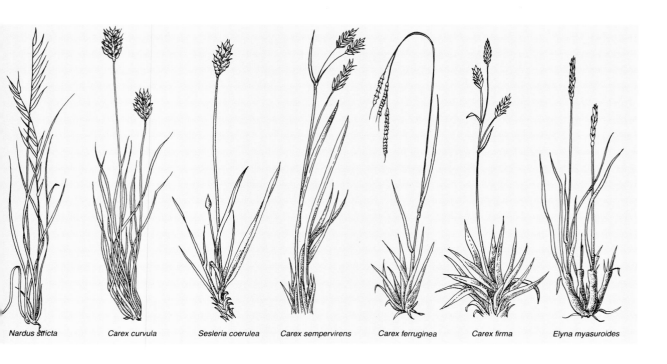

Nardus stricta   Carex curvula   Sesleria coerulea   Carex sempervirens   Carex ferruginea   Carex firma   Elyna myasuroides

Here is another steppelike community (low-growing grasses). It forms the typical "alpine steppe."

Fescue grasslands. Besides valley fescue grass, other plant groupings exist in mountain grazing lands. Here the most common plants belong to the genus *Festuca.* The main species are red fescue, purple melickgrass, Haller's fescue, and variegated fescue. Grasslands with the last two species grow at higher altitudes than trisetum and brome grasslands. The best-known alpine flowers grow in grasslands containing Haller's fescue and variegated fescue. Here alpine and bearded bellflowers, various species of pinks, and a few species of *Potentilla*, especially three-leaf cinquefoil and golden cinquefoil, can be found. In the western and southern Alps, another type of fescue grassland is very common. It has many very colorful species. This is a taller fescue grassland, which has certain species of asphodels and large plants of single-flowered cornflower.

Matgrass grasslands. Red, or Haller's, fescue grasslands change into matgrass grasslands because of livestock. An overly-large herd of grazing cattle will cause a decrease in some species and an increase in others. This is because of trampling and eating. The species which increase certainly include matgrass, which does best of all. This plant spreads until it almost completely covers the ground and forms its own pastureland. Matgrass is a tough grass which invades meadows and is not liked by cattle. As a result, it has no trouble spreading where the soil is poor because of erosion. The soil in a matgrass pasture is very acid at the surface. Few other species can grow here. Among those which remain are arnica, snake root, and blue veronica.

Sedge grasslands. This grouping of grasses grows at the highest altitudes in mountains rich in sand. It is found up to about 10,000 feet (3,000 m). It is the bent sedge grassland, a true climax community. It forms a thick, dark yellow covering at the snow line. It can grow in a very short growth period of no longer than four to five months. Bent sedge is a typical pioneer plant which produces humus (rotted material) in the soil. The result is that the soil in these pastures is fertile and does not dry up easily.

Typical plants in sedge grassland are alpine trefoil, primrose, and Koch's gentian. There is also groundsel in the western Alps, spring anemone growing as high as 11,800 feet (3600 m), and alpine anemone.

Seseli-evergreen grasslands. This is a typical and complete example of grassland occurring in limestone

Opposite page: The so-called "petals" of the famous edelweiss are actually special leaves covered with hairs which protect them from frost. The small yellow "heads" in the middle are the actual clumps of flowers.

Following page: A beautiful flowering gentianella is pictured. The genus *Gentiana* contains many species. They all have bright flowers in blues, yellows, purples, etc. Some species, like yellow gentian, are used for medicine.

54

mountains. It is found at the same altitude zone as the sedge grassland, which grows in sandy soil. This community can grow at high temperatures. It is found where the sun's rays are strongest and where the spring thaw of snow is most rapid. It is named for a grass called "seseli" and for a member of the sedge family called "evergreen sedge." Along with these two species is alpine anemone, Crantz's cinquefoil, violet, and alpine aster. This is the home of edelweiss or lio foot, the best known of alpine plant life.

Rusty sedge grasslands. In limestone mountains, this grouping replaces the seseli-evergreen sedge community on moist north-facing slopes. Rusty sedge often grows with yellow gentian. This yellow-flowered plant has roots used for medicine. Also present are bellflower, the beautiful narcissus-flowered anemone, and two small but highly scented orchids: the common scented nigritella and the red variety.

Tufted sedge grasslands. The tufted sedge grasslands also occur on limestone soil. Tufted sedge is a pioneering plant community at higher altitudes. It occurs on slopes which are dry and rocky, with little snow. At first the vegetation is scattered, then it becomes a thicker covering. Tufted sedge is a plant which can easily be uprooted by the wind, even if it grows in tight clumps. But these sedge clumps are held tight by sturdy dwarf willows and dryas, as well as blue-green saxifrage and its evergreen cousin. These pale green clumps are colored by the bright blue flowers of many kinds of gentianellas, blue snow gentian, the beautiful groundsel, and various other species.

Bristle sedge grasslands. On ridges which are exposed to strong winds, where tufted sedge would not have a chance of surviving, is the bristle sedge community. This plant has bristly, stiff leaves and can live in extreme environmental conditions. These include very large yearly temperature changes and little snow in winter. The species in this community are, therefore, very resistant to drought, wind, and cold. There is also snow pink, alpine pink, tiny gentianella, snow gentian, and others, as well as many types of lichens.

Apennine grasslands. Grasslands, as they have been described for the Alps, are found in all the European mountain systems which reach altitudes similar to those of the Alps. The Apennines do not contain these same plant communities, probably because of the lower altitudes and the different plant species common in their grasslands. In

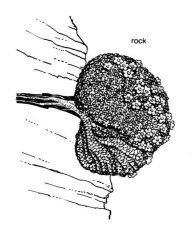

rock

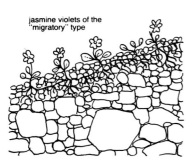

jasmine violets of the "migratory" type

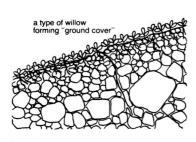

a type of willow forming "ground cover"

Sendtner's poppy, which "stabilizes" the ground

Apennines, where the mountain zone with the beech trees ends, are grasslands. These cannot be called typical alpine grasslands, so they are called "pseudo-alpine" or "alpine-like." They contain taller grasses and plants like tall oat grass, false bromegrass, bracken, orchard grass or cocksfoot, and fall dandelion.

Pseudo-alpine grasslands now occupy the zone which used to be the home of the beech tree. These zones have been reduced in area because of tree cutting, fires, and possibly the drought which has occurred in the area in recent years. Above this "pseudo-alpine" zone are the typical high altitude pasturelands on the uppermost plateau. Various hardy plants have been able to take root in the gravelly soil of these areas.

In the Apennines are the same plant communities that have been described for the Alps but with certain replacements by similar species. Two varieties of seseli, for example, take the ecological place of the seseli species that grow on limestone soils in the Alps. Smooth sedge has taken the place of the evergreen sedge described in the seseli-evergreen pasture of the Alps. The edelweiss's place is taken by the Apennine lion's foot. The much-beloved edelweiss is a small perennial herb that grows high in the Alps. The calcarate violet is replaced by genia's violet, and so on.

Usually the Apennine peaks barely reach the pseudo-alpine altitudes, and those mountains which are higher contain few upland plateaus. In some cases, the slopes can hold little moisture because they are porous and exposed to strong winds, so there is little room left for grassland. These physical and climatic factors, especially wind, rain, and snow, interfere with the natural development of plant communities. Together with overgrazing, especially by sheep, they are the causes of the run-down, poor state into which the high mountain pasturelands of the Apennines are falling.

When the damaged grassy mat of these eroded meadows is leached (soaked) too much by water, a certain fescue grass begins to grow, called *Festuca dimorpha*. With its well-developed root system and tough leaves, it manages to hold the loose soil together. Thus, it protects the gravelly slopes from erosion. Its extremely tough leaves are of no use as fodder for livestock, unfortunately. Once again it appears that the actions of people are contributing to an ecological disaster. In this particular case, the climate increases and worsens the results of human activity.

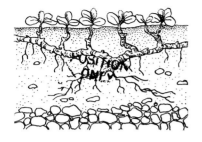

Above: The herbaceous willow is the smallest member of the willow genus. Rarely more than 4 inches (10 cm) tall, it grows in small "snow valleys." It is a typical member of this plant community. It represents an extreme form of adaptation to mountain conditions. In fact, it grows underground, sending only a few leaves and flowers above ground during the brief period of growth activity.

Below: A species of houseleek (with star-shaped pink flowers) is pictured with one of the chickweeds growing on the rocks of Mount Monviso. This is a typical plant group growing on rocks. They manage to take hold in the smallest cracks where only a handful of soil can collect. The houseleek blooms between June and September and lives in soil with a low calcium level.

Vegetation on Rocks and Rubble

The small amount of plant life present on rocky crags, in gravelly moraines, or even on sloping alluvial (river) deposits is composed of very specialized plants. This means they have special features which help them live in difficult places. They are so specialized that they cannot survive outside their rocky environment. In fact, if their seeds fall in grassland or in some other plant community, they will not grow. They will be forced out by the other neighboring plants which rob the soil nutrition from the newcomers.

Vegetation in the Snow

Snow valleys are high altitude depressions where the snow stays on the ground for ten to eleven months of the year. Plants which grow in this environment must have unusual methods for survival. Some of them, for example, show what is called "nanism," meaning that they are dwarf-like in size.

Another method of survival used by the plants in this environment is the absence of seed production or sterility. Instead they reproduce by a process called "vivipary." This is a form of reproduction in which the offspring develop from only one parent as miniature plants, shoots, or bulbs, which then break off.

WILDLIFE

The European continent was covered with broadleaf and coniferous forests up until two thousand years ago. Today, only the mountain regions remain covered with forest. And today, only these regions can provide homes for complete and self-sufficient animal communities.

There are reasons why the mountains have not been harmed by people as much as other areas. The mountain environment has not been settled as much, and the human activity has been centered around farming and small towns. Now many people are moving to lowland towns and cities. This is also helping to reduce human effects in mountain areas and return meadows and grasslands to their natural vegetation.

Creatures like deer and badgers, roebucks, and weasels could live in all of Europe. But today, they are mostly found in places that are difficult for people to reach and where the altitude is not very high. The wildlife or fauna of the mountain chains also includes a certain number of "refugees" from the lowlands. But there are many mountain species that are not found in the lowlands.

Origins of Alpine Wildlife

Many of the vertebrates (animals with backbones) which used to live in southern Europe are today only found in the Alps. They once roamed over the entire continent until perhaps ten thousand years ago, during the last glaciation. The same is also true of invertebrates (animals without a backbone) and plants. When the climate became milder and the ice retreated, these species followed the cold northward, leaving behind the so-called relict, or leftover, populations. These populations usually have related species or subspecies farther north. Sometimes the time of separation between the two has been long enough to produce different subspecies (a variety of a species). This is true with the rock pipit, a small insect-eating bird which nests between the shrub-covered region and the snow line. Its cousin is the water pipit, which lives along the northern coastline of Europe, where there is a cold climate.

There are many such cases of separate distribution for populations of the same species. The more a mountain animal has adapted to low temperatures, the more distinct the mountain and northern populations have become. This is because mixing between the populations will not often happen since the mountain variety will stay in the mountains.

An excellent example of this can be found in the grouse

Opposite page: The lynx is the largest cat and one of the largest carnivores (meat-eaters) in Europe. It has already been wiped out in several areas. Today, it survives mainly in the Carpathians and the Spanish Sierra Nevadas, where a slightly different variety lives. It has recently been successfully released into the Austrian Alps.

Below: The present-day distribution areas of the black grouse *(top)*, the capercaillie or wood grouse *(center)*, and the willow grouse or ptarmigan *(bottom)* are shown by the shaded areas. By comparing the three, the increasing separation of the European populations can be seen.

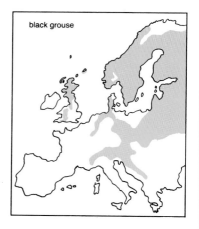

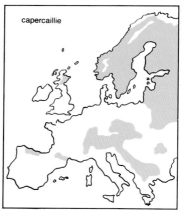

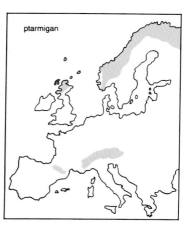

family. It is possible to identify a typical series of events which leads to the separation of populations. The distribution of the black grouse or blackcock covers an area that extends from the mountains of southern Europe to northern Europe. But there is still communication between the populations at both ends. The distribution of the wood grouse, or capercaillie, has divided into several parts. In the southern part of the area, it tends to follow mountain ranges. In the north, it is found in highland areas. The distribution of the willow grouse, or ptarmigan, is widely separated. In the south, this bird is found on the upper mountain slopes of the

A group of male ibex wanders on a hillside. This species has been saved from extinction and now lives in the Gran Paradiso National Park, which was once a royal game reserve. The ibex has been released into various other parts of the Alps.

Alps and Pyrenees. In the north, it occurs in northern Scotland, Scandinavia, and Iceland.

This same distribution area is shared by mammals such as the blue, or mountain, hare and a rather strange bat called "Nilsson's serotine." Usually bats attract little interest or attention from people. They are considered ugly and have a bad reputation. They also have nighttime habits. The small serotine has a maximum length of just over 2 inches (54 millimeters) and is not really very ugly. It does not have the leaflike flap which, to the human eye, makes the faces of some other bats so odd. Its adaptation to cold climates is

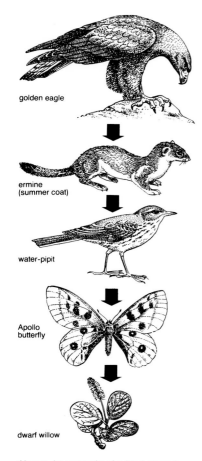

golden eagle

ermine
(summer coat)

water-pipit

Apollo
butterfly

dwarf willow

Above: An example of a food chain is illustrated.

Opposite page: An example of a food web can be quite complicated. The marten *(bottom, right)* may behave like a primary consumer when it eats berries, or as a secondary consumer when it eats small rodents. It may also become a tertiary consumer, preying on insect-eating birds. The same is true of the black woodpecker *(top right)*, the coal titmouse *(perched in the middle of the picture)* and the squirrel *(center left)*. All of these creatures feed on plants and other small animals. The goshawk, which has caught a squirrel *(top left)*, may also be called a secondary consumer because it preys on herbivores, and a tertiary consumer because it preys on other predators. On the other hand, the crossbill *(center top)* and the bullfinch *(center, below the crossbill)* both fit into the simple classification of primary consumers. These birds are specialized for eating pine seeds and shoots, respectively. The ground beetle *(bottom left)* specializes in feeding on other insects.

unusual in the bat family. In fact, it turns out to be the most northerly of the entire group of European species. It is the only one living far above the sixtieth parallel, almost to the very north of Scandinavia. During the winter months, the serotine leaves its home. It goes on long migratory flights similar to those of many birds which live in northern areas. It flies to the mountains of Switzerland, Austria, and northeast Italy.

To finish discussion on the origins of the vertebrates of the Alps today, the most "noble" creatures living there should be considered. These animals are the real symbols of mountain wildlife. They include the large wild goat called the ibex and the small goatlike antelope called the chamois. These two species occur only in Europe, and they do not have a northern cousin. The most acceptable hypothesis is that these species originated in Asia and reached the Alps during the periods of glaciation. It seems very likely that the same thing happened with the marmot, a large member of the rodent family.

The Food Chain

All of the animal and plant species living in the same area form specific and clearly recognized ecological communities called "ecosystems." The term *ecosystem* became commonly used when people began to understand the active relationships between the different residents of any specific natural environment. The species which occupy the same environment are affected by the presence of the others, and each one in turn affects the others. The simplest illustration of these relationships is now known as the "food chain." Plants get energy from the sun. Herbivores, which are plant-eating animals, get the energy they need by eating plants. Carnivores, which are meat-eating animals, get their energy by eating herbivores or other carnivores. This describes how things work but very simply.

A description which relates more to nature could be called a "food web," a complex tangle in which the individual food chains form links and connections. The plants are the foundation of the web. Next are the primary consumers, those animals which eat any part of any plant. The upper connections are occupied by the secondary consumers, those animals which eat other animals. But because many species feed on both animal and plant foods, each connection is associated with many others. The picture then becomes more complicated, like a web.

MAMMALS

Even if the mountain environment is among the best places for encountering these creatures, it is rare to actually come face to face with mammals, large or small. This is partly because almost all of them lead a nocturnal life, and partly because all the species try to avoid meeting humans. Still, a trained eye will manage to see signs of animal life in the form of footprints, lairs, and dens. With a little patience and care, the beginner will soon learn to identify signs of the animals, even if the surroundings at first look quite unlived in. Of course, the larger mammals live in the most hard-to-reach places. But a simple walking trip into any woods found near a town or village can yield results. Here it is possible to get a glimpse of the small species which bring life to the countryside.

Small Mammals

These small creatures are not often visible because of their shy habits, but they are still needed in nature's overall plan for mountain life. In fact, they are the main source of food for a wide range of other mammals, birds, and meat-eating reptiles.

There are many kinds of small mammals. Some belong to the insect-eating groups, such as various shrews. There are rodents, such as squirrels, water voles, and field or sood mice. Four European rodents of the Gliridae family are the dormouse, the hazel mouse, the forest dormouse, and the tree mouse. Usually these species are not found at high altitudes, but some of them may live as high as 6,560 feet (2,000 m) and beyond. Examples are moles, tree mice, and yellow-necked field mice. Among the few small mammals which are completely alpine are the mountain shrew, a species of water shrew, and the snow vole. These three species are all found only in the Alps and one or two other mountain chains.

The mountain shrew lives mostly in the moist areas of coniferous forests; while its cousin, the water shrew, likes moist but grassy places, close to ponds and pools. Both of them are easy to identify by their pointed faces and the gray color on their backs. They spend part of their lives in underground tunnels. Using plant material, they build nests which become home for the adults and nursery for the young. The rest of their time is spent looking for food on the ground or in water. When it returns from the hunt, the water shrew also uses its underground passages to clean itself. It will scurry through the maze of tunnels, which are just large

Opposite page: The hazel mouse is the smallest European dormouse. In mountains, it will not venture above the deciduous broadleaf tree line. It builds a ball-shaped nest. Here it rears its young and spends the winter in hibernation.

The tree mouse is a friendly dormouse with a mask on its face and a black-and-white brushlike tail. In the Alps, as elsewhere, it lives in forests. It often builds a cozy shelter using old birds' nests or natural hollows, which it lines with moss.

enough for it. This brushes the water from its fur as it goes. Before long, it is completely dry.

Of the small mammals, the species which reaches the highest altitudes is the snow vole. It will sometimes even live beyond the 13,000-foot mark (4,000 m). It seldom lives below 5,000 feet (1,500 m). Oddly enough, this vole likes the sun. Its usual movements take place during the daytime, when the weather turns nice. It probably lives this way because of the low nighttime temperatures at these altitudes. It is light gray, 4 to 5 inches (11 to 14 cm) long, and has a very short tail, like all voles. It lives on rocky slopes, in the rhododendron zone, and in stony grasslands and open woodlands. It is not very wild at all.

Back below the tree line are many other species, including those "woodland elves," the dormice. The most common species are the dormouse proper and the hazel mouse. But the other two species, the forest dormouse and tree mouse, are more typical of the mountains. They are also found in coniferous woods, since they seem to like the Norway spruce. The forest dormouse occurs in the northern Tyrol and in the Dinaric Alps in Yugoslavia, almost always

at altitudes of 2,100 to 5,200 feet (650 to 1,600 m). But they have also been seen much higher up, in rocky areas where there are absolutely no trees at all. The tree mouse may not venture quite so high, but it occurs throughout the alpine chain up to the tree line. Of all four members of the dormouse group, it has the brightest coat and a black mask, which gives it a lively expression. Like the dormouse proper, the forest dormouse has an overall gray color.

Finally, of the small mammals which venture to the edge of the tree line, the squirrel, the most beautiful and the largest of all the woodland-dwelling rodents, must not be overlooked.

The squirrel is the only completely plant-eating species and the only one with daytime habits. It will live happily in any woods which are in good condition. Its presence is made obvious by the piles of pine cones beneath conifers, which have been broken open and emptied of their seeds.

The Mountain Hare

A white fur coat is the very best disguise for moving about in the snow without being noticed. The mountain hare uses its coat in this way to avoid attack from its natural

The European squirrel has two basic colorings: red and dark-coated. In the Alps, the red variety is more common, but it is still quite easy to spot a dark-coated cousin.

67

enemies, especially the golden eagle. This important fur color developed during the period of glaciation and has remained in both the northern variety and the smaller southern subspecies.

The mountain, or blue, hare starts to change its normal bluish brown fur in November. This is when the temperature drops and the first snow falls on the mountain peaks. Within one month, the hare becomes completely white, except for a thin black stripe around the eyes and the tips of the ears. In April, it will once again grow its summer coat when the snow starts to melt.

The mountain hare's favorite environment is the edge of a forest. Here it finds its ideal foods, such as shoots, branches, and pieces of bark. There it also finds good hiding places among bushes or roots. Because it does not dig a burrow, the hare must rear its young in natural hollows in the ground. The young are born twice a year after a development period of fifty days. Young hares are born with their eyes open, a coat of fur, and the ability to run. This is the main difference between hares and rabbits, whose young are born with eyes closed, no fur, and helpless.

The Marmot

Marmots are at least 20 inches (50 cm) in length and weigh up to 4 pounds (2 kilograms). They have rounded heads and short tails and are rather stout looking. Despite this, and even though their normal walking looks rather unsteady, they are quite nimble. They can climb up and down cliffs and rocks with sure-footed ease.

They live in colonies, which contain at least a dozen

Marmots are typical residents of the Alps. They are well known for their alarm whistles and their upright sitting position *(shown on the left)*. The young often have mock fights in which they push and pull at each other. These fights may end with both of them rolling down a slope *(center)*. The adults, on the other hand, engage in rituals which resemble duels. The "fighters" face each other, sit upright, and twitter loudly *(right)*.

Opposite page: A group of three adult stags (male deer) walks with a young deer. In this species, as with most hoofed mammals, separate herds are usually formed. These are made up of adult males and females with young that are less than one year old. "Harems" are herds of females which live as a group throughout the year. They will only accept the stag in the mating season, which is called the "rut."

68

individuals. Marmot colonies live in burrows dug about 6 feet (2 m) below ground. They live in clearings at altitudes of between 5,000 and 10,000 feet (1,500 to 3,050 m). Usually, marmots are peaceful animals. If they are the least bit frightened, they make an unusual whistling sound while sitting up on their hind legs. The colonies separate into pairs which dig their own burrows at the end of the winter. This is when their hibernation is over and the mating season begins. In early June, the young are born, two to four per litter. They stay with their mother until the following summer.

The young spend all day playing. They are watched over by an adult, ready to give the alarm should it see a

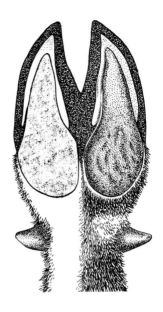

predator approaching. Young marmots may be attacked by golden eagles and foxes, which will sometimes attack adults as well. They are also among the favorite prey of eagle owls, ravens, and martens. The marmot diet is completely made up of plants. Its favorite foods are aromatic and juicy plants or roots, but if there is nothing else available, it will also eat the common grasses around its lair. These same grasses are stored as hay to line the winter burrow, where the marmot shuts itself away when autumn comes.

Hoofed Mammals

The name *ungulates* describes those hoofed mammals which have modified metacarpals and metatarsals. These are the sets of bones which are like the human bones in the palm of the hand and the foot. In this mammal group, these are long bones which support the legs and transfer body

Above: The structure of a chamois hoof, typical of the hoofed mammals or ungulates, is pictured. Support is provided by the last bones of the third and fourth toes. These are covered with a tough material. It supports the entire weight of the body. The split or cloven hoof doubles the number of points of support as the animal moves. In snow, the toes can spread out and provide a wider supporting surface. On ice, the points act like spikes or crampons.

Right: An adult roebuck reaches for leaves. This stag's antlers have grown as large as they can in this species.

Opposite page: The growth and replacement of a stag's antlers are presented in different stages. A mature stag's antlers weigh many pounds. Replacing them every year requires a great deal of body effort. A large amount of food is used for their growth. In fact, a stag will use about as much energy to replace its antlers as a female will use during the gestation period. The antlers grow from a bony base which sticks up from the stag's forehead, even when the antlers have just been shed.

weight onto the hooves. But not all ungulates are alike in these bones. Differences in these bones exist in different species and are the result of modifications for various ways of life.

The large herbivores which live in the European mountains belong to the group of ungulates called "artiodactyls." This group has a two-part, or cloven, hoof. It is actually an enlargement of the third and fourth toes such as typical five-toed mammals have. The first toe is missing, while the second and the fifth toes are either missing or else are very small. A leg designed in this way is well suited for moving about in rough mountainous areas, even if the large size of some of these mammals, like the ibex, might make them seem clumsy. The cloven hoof actually increases the nimbleness and strength of the animal's movements. The structure of the hoof allows the animal to have eight points of support (two on each leg) on the ground. The bottom of the hoof is flexible for clinging. The hard point of the hoof acts as a spike or crampon, keeping the animal from slipping. A slip in these rocky environments could easily mean death.

Four species of artiodactyls live in the Alps. The deer and the roebuck belong to the Cervidae family, while the ibex and the chamois belong to the Bovidae family. Their shapes are distinct, and they can easily be identified a long way off with binoculars. The first recognizable feature is the pair of antlers or horns which these mammals carry on their foreheads. This feature makes it immediately possible to

identify the animal according to species.

In the Cervidae, or deer family, the antlers are rather branched. They are shed and regrown each year, which requires a lot of food. During the growth stage, the antlers are covered with a layer of skin and fur called "velvet." After the antlers are fully grown, this is shed, leaving the bare bony antler. The velvet, which contains many blood vessels, carries the food needed for the growth of the antlers. After the growth is complete, the velvet dries and dies, falling off in pieces. This process causes itching for the animal. It will often rub its antlers against tree trunks and branches to get some relief. Peeled bark, especially on younger trees, is evidence of this activity, which occurs mainly in the spring. The antlers are shed at the end of autumn, after the mating season, or rut. They contain a store of valuable animal protein which is eaten by various rodents, including squirrels. This is why antlers that have been shed are seldom found.

Every spring, the antlers gain a new branch, up to a limit of ten or so for the stag and three for the smaller roebuck. The females of these species, or does, do not have antlers, but they can be told apart by their size. A female deer is at least 40 inches high (1 m) at the shoulder, while a female roebuck does not measure more than 30 inches (75 cm). The roebuck also has a permanent white marking on the rump which is easily seen in winter.

In the Bovidae family, unlike the Cervidae, the "antlers" are not branched and can correctly be called horns. They are permanent and have a tough protein covering all year round. This covering also helps determine the age of each individual. At the rear of the very strong horns of the ibex is a notch for each year of age. In the chamois, on the other hand, each passing year is indicated by a small step at the base of the horny coverings. In the Bovidae, the females also have horns, though they are smaller than those of the males.

The main feature of an animal's adaptation to its environment is how its reproductive cycles are timed with the seasons. The mating season occurs at a certain time of year so that all of the young are born when food is most plentiful, in May and June. The longer the gestation period, the earlier mating occurs.

The stag makes bellowing calls, known as "bells," to attract females in early autumn. Because of the size of this species of deer, it takes eight and a half months before the baby fawn is born. The chamois and ibex require about six

An Abruzzi chamois is seen wearing its summer coat. This population has a much lighter coat than the more common alpine subspecies. The difference is even more visible in winter. There is also some difference in size. The Abruzzi variety is slightly smaller, with horns that are more arched. This animal was probably once common throughout the Apennines. Today, its numbers have been reduced to four or five thousand living only in Abruzzi National Park.

months, which is why their harems of females are formed later, almost at the beginning of winter. The roebuck is once again the exception to the rule. It has a very unusual mating pattern. It mates in summer and, at first glance, seems to have the longest gestation period. But at the beginning of pregnancy, the development of the embryo is actually interrupted for several months. This is called the "pregestation" period. Females that have not been fertilized during the summer may have a second heat (the period when females are ready to mate) in the autumn. In this case, there is no unusually long gestation, and the young are born after only five months.

The hoofed mammals in the Alps have the same type of diet. They all feed on nearly every part of tender plants growing in the mountains: grasses, berries, stems, leaves,

The wolf is intelligent and has complex social behavior patterns. This is because this predator lives and hunts in a pack. In its relationships with other wolves, its behavior is like that of dogs. Examples include the positions showing superiority and submission shown in the illustration on the next page. These signals, sent from one member of the species to another, help calm hostile individuals. They are important in all predatory species that live in groups because they help weaker individuals survive. These individuals also have their part to play in the hunt.

and even the small branches and woody tips of shrubs and trees. The four types of hoofed mammals described here share the same general environment but not the same resources within that environment. Typically, the ibex lives in the highest regions. This wild goat can be considered the most alpine of the four species. At lower altitudes is the chamois, which is forced to live there by competition with the other species. It lives more at the edges of the forest. The forest itself would be constantly occupied by the deer and the roebuck, but the roebuck is less particular. It can stand human presence better than the ibex or chamois and ven-

tures farther down into valleys.

Human interference with nature, past and present, greatly affects the areas of distribution of these animals. This is especially obvious with the ibex. It has barely escaped extinction, thanks to the protection it received in the Gran Paradiso "Royal Hunting Reserve" in 1856. Now there are some fifteen thousand animals, divided into about 150 groups or colonies. They live among the mountaintops of Val d'Aosta, Piedmont, Austria, and certain Swiss states called "cantons." About three thousand more animals are scattered through the other countries of the alpine chain.

The original parents of these ibex groups came from the Swiss population, which is now the largest. It began directly from the Gran Paradiso herd. In Italy, this herd is still the most constant, numbering 3,200 animals.

The chamois is distributed fairly uniformly throughout the Alps. It is also found in the Carpathians, the Tatry Mountains, the Jura Mountains, the Balkans, and the Caucasus. It has also been released into the Vosges Forest in France and the Black Forest in West Germany. A different looking subspecies, the Abruzzi chamois, is found in Abruzzi National Park in the central Apennines. Its body is slimmer, and its horns are slightly longer and less curved. Along with the subspecies of chamois now living in the Pyrenees, it is the last remaining population of chamois which existed during the Riss glaciation 200,000 years ago.

Carnivores

The hoofed mammals are the largest herbivores in Europe. As a result, they are the favorite prey for large carnivores. Hoofed mammals make up part of the diet of bears, wolves, and lynxes. Strange though it may seem, these killers perform a very useful service in nature's overall plan. By preying on wild hoofed mammals, they keep the populations of hoofed mammals at a constant level. Also, the carnivores usually kill weaker or sick individuals, which would probably die anyway.

For hundreds of years, people wrongly thought that any kind of wild beast was an enemy and a dangerous rival. All that remains of these creatures are very small, scattered groups. In the countries of central Europe, people are trying to replace the natural activity of carnivores by using selective hunting. Only certain species and numbers of animals may be killed. This will keep their population levels fairly constant. But human interference can not easily replace the

Brown bears usually move about slowly, dragging their feet. This gives them the appearance of being peaceful and rather sluggish. But when necessary, they can be amazingly nimble and fast moving. They often live alone. This is because of their small European populations. They will only gather in groups near large sources of food or to rear young. Young bears stay with their mother for quite a long time.

The fox has perhaps the most varied feeding habits of the carnivores. It may eat ants and small animals or other mammals larger than itself. It will also eat people's garbage. Because it can adapt so well, it is now one of the most common predators in Europe.

service the predators perform. These animals have a relationship with the creatures they prey upon which has existed for thousands of years.

There was a time when the brown bear lived throughout Europe, except in Iceland and the Mediterranean islands. This distribution shows that the brown bear was at first more connected with plant life than with altitude. But little by little, it has been forced to take refuge in mountains. Today the only remains of a once large population of brown bears are isolated groups scattered here and there. In the Alps there may be only a dozen or so brown bears left. They live inside the Adamello-Brenta Nature Park. In the Abruzzi National Park, there are about a hundred bears.

Wolves vanished from the Alps long ago. In western Europe, the only other country which still has a fairly large population is Spain. Here there are about two hundred wolves, about twice as many as in Italy. To avoid humans, the Apennine wolves always stay high in the mountains, above 2,600 to 3,300 feet (800 to 1,000 m). Like the bear, their habits have become mainly nocturnal. Usually wolves do not move about in groups of more than ten individuals.

The third large carnivore mentioned earlier is the lynx. This animal completely vanished from Italy and the entire alpine chain at the beginning of the 1900s. In Europe, it now seems to live only in the mountain ranges of Spain, in the Carpathians, and in parts of Russia and Scandinavia.

The ermine is a small bundle of viciousness. The alpine subspecies is less than 8 inches (20 cm) long, but it can kill animals three times its own size, such as the hare. It also hunts in groups. For an animal of its size, it makes a surprising amount of noise. The tip of its tail is bushy and black in both summer and winter. This is the main difference between the ermine and the weasel.

The lynx has a very short tail and two unusual clumps of hair sticking up from the tips of its ears. It is a large animal, reaching a length of 50 inches (130 cm), not counting the tail, and a height of 30 inches (75 cm). It can weigh more than 77 pounds (35 kg). It preys on hoofed mammals and birds of the grouse family.

Besides these three large carnivores, the fox must be included. The fox is not found just in mountainous areas, but is the most widespread carnivore in Europe. Also important are the seven species of the weasel family. Except for the badger and the otter, all of the members of the weasel family seem to be specially designed for raiding the burrows and nests of rodents, which form the bulk of their diets. The weasel family members have very short legs, narrow, limber bodies, and small ears held close to their heads.

BIRDS

It is common for mammals to move around at night. Most birds, however, are active during the day. Because birds are so easy to spot, they are among the first animals to catch the attention of the nature lover. Among the birds, there are as many types of behavior as with the carnivores. But there are many more species of birds, and birds are also more brightly colored. This is because they are usually active in the day, when their colors send out different signals. Colors are also used in their mating habits. The males put on displays to mark out their territories during the mating season. If a bird species has dull coloring, it probably has a loud and unusual song instead. Then it will use its song to mark out its territory.

Birds of Prey

In the bird world, the predator's role is played mainly by two groups of species. The first is the falcon group, or Falconiformes, and includes the diurnal birds of prey. The other is the owl group, or Strigïformes, and includes the nocturnal birds of prey. It is not unusual to come across several birds of prey on a climb up a mountainside. But few species are found only at the higher altitudes.

Even the majestic golden eagle, the best known of all birds of prey, has had to retreat into the highest mountains. This is because people have advanced on nature and destroyed the eagle's habitats. Today, golden eagles nest at altitudes between 5,250 and 5,900 feet (1,600 to 1,800 m). Sometimes they will even nest at an altitude as high as 8,200 feet (2,500 m).

In the Alps, there is a constant golden eagle population of about five hundred male and female pairs. The population is constant because the birds are in good health. This is due to the protection which they have today. But there is little chance for the population to grow and expand, unless it spreads to other high mountain ranges.

A pair of golden eagles usually has several nests. They are scattered over a territory of about 40 sq. miles (100 sq. km). But in any one year, they will only use one of their nests. These are built below the uppermost tree line. The pair usually builds its nests on ledges on rock walls. Nests built in trees are not typical. The eagle's hunting territories are higher up, where hoofed mammals graze and marmots have their burrows. The eagle's diet includes young chamois, young ibex, kid goats, and marmots. Eagles hunt these prey for themselves and their young during the summer months.

Opposite page: The eagle owl is the largest of the European owls, often growing 28 inches (70 cm) tall, with a wingspan of 63 inches (160 cm). It lives in isolated places, nesting in cracks in rocks or on the ground. Sometimes it may nest in natural hollows in large trees. But the eagle owl is quite rare. Only sixty pairs were found nesting in the Swiss Alps in 1976.

The golden eagle builds its nests well out of reach on rock walls. Both parents are involved in building the nest and in rearing their young. In the rearing period, food for the young is provided mainly by the male bird. After about three months, the nestlings take to the air. But they will not be able to reproduce until they are four years old.

The golden eagle is the only large predator which is still active throughout the Alps. In the winter, the only prey available to it are hares and grouse. In rare cases, eagles may become "superpredators," which are predators that catch other predators, and catch a fox or some other bird of prey. The animal caught will often weigh more than the eagle itself. But the eagle has no trouble carrying the prey on a downhill flight back to the nest.

Within twelve weeks, from May to August, the young eaglet grows as large as its parents. It measures about 32 inches (80 cm) long and has a wingspan of almost 7 feet (2 m). At this age it is ready to fly. The young bird is different

from the adults because of its white feathers beneath the tail and wings. These white markings disappear after the bird reaches sexual maturity. This usually happens at the age of four years. From then on its plumage will be brown all over, with lighter, almost golden feathers on the back of the neck.

Members of the falcon group rarely get up to high altitudes. It is much easier to find them lower down, where there are more rodents and small birds. On a walk, it is quite easy to watch a kestrel, or sparrow-hawk, or goshawk searching for prey from above. With luck, an observer might also see a catch, with the bird swooping at high speed down to the ground to grab its victim.

The bird best designed for this type of attack is the peregrine falcon. It is a stout bird with a squared-off tail and pointed wings. This falcon can dive through the air at speeds faster than 150 miles (250 km) per hour.

Autumn offers an amazing sight. During the migratory period, birds cross the Alps and other mountain chains on their journey southward. People may find themselves beneath groups of ten or more large birds of prey. Birds such as buzzards or honey buzzards can be seen on their way to areas where they will spend the winter. This also happens close to the large lakes in the lower alpine areas. Here there may be birds such as brown kites.

At one time, vultures lived throughout the Alps. Today, there are small numbers of these birds in the mountains of Spain and the Balkans. A number of griffon vultures can also be found in Sardinia. These griffons make a late summer appearance in the Tauern Range of Austria. They come from the Dalmatian area of Yugoslavia. Most of these griffon vultures are young birds. They have been forced to leave their birthplace because the few territories available are already overcrowded. When they reach Austria, they scatter and die, without reproducing. Attempts to have them settle in the Tauern Range have so far been unsuccessful. The European black vulture and the lammergeyer or bearded vulture have vanished totally from the Alps. This is due to destructive hunting practices and prejudice on the part of local people. These vultures have been mercilessly persecuted over the years.

The only birds of prey which can really be called permanent residents of Europe's mountain forests are two of the smallest members of the owl group. These are the pygmy owl and the boreal, or Tengmalm's, owl. Pygmy owls measure only about 6 inches (15 cm), about the size of a

Above: The boreal owl lives mainly in beech woods and evergreen forests. Here it can find holes made in large tree trunks by the largest of the European woodpeckers, the black woodpecker. The boreal owl then lays three to four eggs between April and June. The eggs hatch after twenty-five days. The young can fly thirty-five days after hatching.

kestrel

peregrine falcon

sparrow hawk

goshawk

buzzard

golden eagle

Below: Flight drawings of the most common diurnal birds of prey found in European mountains are provided. The least common are the European black vulture and the griffon vulture. Today these birds are found only in mountainous parts of the Mediterranean islands and in the Pyrenees.

robin. The boreal owl is slightly larger, reaching 10 inches (25 cm), like a large blackbird or thrush. Its head is more rounded and its tail is shorter in proportion to its body. The pygmy owl's tail is broad and often opened like a fan above its back.

The favorite environment for these owls is mature evergreen forest. This is where they live in northern and southern Europe. They build their nests in old trees with plenty of holes in them. The pygmy owl may use nests left by woodpeckers. Because of the boreal owl's size, it must watch out for larger nesting holes made by the largest member of the woodpecker family, the black woodpecker.

Pygmy and boreal owls are two tiny predators. In a twenty-four hour day, one or the other of them is always on the hunt, as if taking turns. The pygmy owl is active during the daylight and twilight hours, which is unusual for an owl. Boreal owls only hunt by night. Pygmy owls eat mainly birds, while the boreal owl eats small mammals. One look at their strong talons and powerful hooked beaks makes it clear that they are designed for predation. But they would be less successful hunters if they did not also have three other important features found in all the species in this group. Their eyes are located in the front of the heads. This gives them a stereoscopic or three-dimensional view of

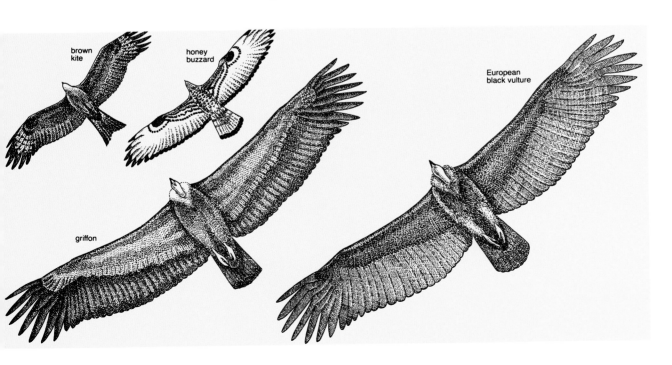

brown kite

honey buzzard

European black vulture

griffon

their surroundings, even when the light is poor. This is necessary to allow them to move about swiftly and safely even at night. It also helps the bird of prey to avoid objects between it and its victim. The second feature is the unequal position of the ear openings, which are surrounded by feathery rings. Like the outside of the human ear, these rings are designed to pick up and amplify sounds. The unequal position helps these birds to clearly hear where an animal is from its slightest movement. Third, the act of actually catching the prey is made easier by the distinctive fringelike shape of the wing feathers. These flight feathers are called "remiges" or "wing quills." This feature allows the owl to fly without making a sound.

All the members of the owl group are greatly feared by small forest animals because of their hunting skills. If an owl makes its cry, the nighttime chattering of dormice in the spring months will stop at once. In daylight, if a small bird comes upon a nocturnal bird of prey resting, it will react in such a way that birds of many different species immediately gang together. They all make a terrific racket and disturb the predator until it leaves its perch and finds a quieter spot.

There are also many larger species of owls. But these birds like mixed woodland where there are plenty of natural hollows to use. The hoot of an owl can almost always be heard in the woods at night. Sometimes in winter, the pygmy owl and the boreal owl join in the "choir," leaving their own territory and flying to lower altitudes to find food. The eagle owl, which is the most beautiful of all the owls, has the deepest and most eerie hoot.

Grouse

The members of the grouse family, or Tetraonidae, can be called the most typical birds found in mountainous regions. They are well adapted to the cold climate in these parts. This can be seen by their nostrils, which are covered by a layer of feathers to reduce the amount of cold air that enters. This feature only occurs in this group. Another special feature of the grouse is two bright red patches of skin above the eyes of males. These patches, called "caruncles," are used as mating signals.

The willow grouse, or ptarmigan, was left in its present location by the last glaciation period. This bird has the

A female wood grouse or, capercaillie, is very hard to approach, even though it is one of the largest grouse species living in the Alps. It is especially rare to see the female, which lives in the thickest evergreen forests where the undergrowth is very thick. During the mating season, it is possible to get quite close to male birds. These birds sing their loud "love calls" from open areas. In one morning, they will make these calls up to five hundred times.

For the blackcock, the mating season starts in April or May and lasts until June. During this period, the males gather together in special meetings called "leks." Each one of them marks out a small territory of its own. The bird then puts on its own courtship display, at the same time as all the others. First, it spreads its tail feathers and puffs out the caruncles, while strutting about, making high leaps into the air every now and then. During their display, the males also put on a "musical show" in a different posture. With their tails flattened and their wings spread, they stretch their necks and head forward, puffing out their feathers as much as possible. Their loud song is made louder by air sacs on the sides of the neck. This is the first signal that attracts the females toward the mating site. During these displays, it is common to see fierce fights between neighboring males. They are often injured or stunned.

smallest distribution area and the most distinct environment. It lives above 6,560 feet (2,000 m). In the summer months, however, it will move more than 3,000 feet (1,000 m) higher, close to the 10,000-foot (3,000 m) mark. It nests in steep, rocky places or on fairly flat ground that has many boulders. Here the ptarmigan can find good hiding places. It is not very fussy about food and will eat almost any type of plant matter that it finds at these altitudes. It is not greatly affected by the coming of winter when its diet changes from fresh plants to frozen plants. These it finds by digging deep tunnels in the snow.

Its plumage follows the change of the seasons. In winter, except for the tail, it becomes completely white. Even more important is the fact that its legs and feet become entirely covered with feathers. In this way, the ptarmigan has broader support because its feet and legs together are like snowshoes.

Other members of the grouse family have similar but not identical adaptations. In the autumn months, they develop two "combs" (made of thin pieces of protein) on the

sides of their toes. These make it easier for the grouse to move about in snow. The combs also keep them from sliding around on ice. In the grouse family, the ptarmigan is the most obvious mountain bird. The other species of grouse stay closer to evergreen forests, which mark the limit of the lower mountain zone. As a result, their diet is different. They eat mostly evergreen needles and stems. Only the young birds need animal protein. They get this by catching tiny invertebrates, their favorite being red ants.

The camouflage for grouse in this lower environment is not provided by white plumage, but by speckled black-and-white feathers. Female birds hatch the eggs and rear the young without help from the male. The young have a speckled coloring which is found in various species.

The different types of grouse are different in size. The female wood grouse, or capercaillie, measures 24 inches (60 cm), whereas the male reaches 34 inches (85 cm). The female black grouse measures 16 inches (40 cm), and the female hazel hen 14 inches (35 cm). The males of these species are easy to identify. They all have brightly-colored plumage, which they use in courtship rituals. The male capercaillie is blackish gray, with a shiny blue-green "bib" and a large black tail which it can spread like a fan. The black grouse or blackcock has an overall bluish color with a lyre-shaped tail. Both of these species have dark brown wings. The male hazel grouse, or hazel hen, is less brightly colored and has a simpler courtship ceremony. The only features that distinguish it from the female are a black marking on the throat and a small crest on the head. In the ptarmigan, the male is like the female except for a black stripe that runs over the eyes. Both parents help in rearing their young.

The capercaillie and the blackcock have the two most complicated and unusual forms of courtship. The male blackcocks gather in early May in clearings or other open spaces where the vegetation is low. These spaces are rarely below 5,000 feet (1,525 m) and are called "arenas." The males strut about these arenas with their chests puffed up and their wings and tails spread wide open. Every now and then they jump up into the air and make a loud noise with their wings. Their song is also very loud. It is made with the neck stretched forward, even with the ground. During these antics, the females wander between the different territories which the males are claiming.

The capercaillie is even noisier. It has the habit of

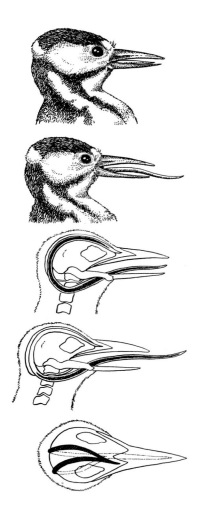

The woodpeckers are specialized birds. Their diet consists mainly of the larvae of wood-eating insects. Pecking activities in tree trunks signal their search for this very specific food. They look for these larvae in the holes they make and catch them with their long, sticky tongues. Usually the tongue is kept folded away inside a cavity which runs completely around the bird's head *(see above)*. During its search, the woodpecker pounds on tree trunks with a distinctive beat. Then it pecks away where the trunk sounds hollow. Here it is sure to find tunnels which contain insects. It eats large numbers of these and gathers many of them at one time in its beak, as can be seen with the great spotted woodpecker *(opposite page)*. The woodpecker's hammering is also important as a means of communication during the period of courtship and mating.

making its cry from exposed but far-off places. If another male appears, there will be a violent fight. This bird is so mean tempered that it has been known to attack people straying into its territory. When it sings, its neck is held up high, the head is tipped back, and the tail is fanned out completely. The sound it makes is throaty and very loud. It can be heard miles away. Usually the song is divided into two "verses." During the second one, the bird makes a great leap into the air. The ceremony begins before dawn and may be repeated more than five hundred times each morning. Mating takes place with all those attracted by the male's display.

In southern Europe, there is another member of this family living in mountains. This is the rock, or Greek, partridge. It belongs to the pheasant group, like domestic chickens. The rock partridge is part of the wildlife of the eastern Mediterranean. It has now become a resident of mountain habitats. It is only found in the Apennines and in the Alps, including the Dinaric Range. In these mountains, its favorite habitats are areas of shrubs and trees which are not too thick and on south-facing slopes. It will also venture above the tree line but returns to lower altitudes with the first snow. It usually nests at altitudes of between 5,250 and 8,200 feet (1,600 to 2,500 m). The female lays her eggs in two nests which are close together. One of these will be taken care of by the male. So male rock partridges play a much more important part in the reproductive process than the males of the other species.

Woodpeckers

Many of the animals living in woodlands, such as rodents, nocturnal birds of prey, titmice, and many more, have woodpeckers to thank for their homes. Woodpeckers are constantly at work. All eight species, pecking away in mountain woodlands, will open up a new nest in some tree about once every year. Their old holes, meanwhile, will be occupied by other animals.

One species of woodpecker is especially interesting because it lives in northern mountain areas. This is the three-toed woodpecker. Unlike the other species which have four toes, this woodpecker has only three toes on each foot. Also, all of the other species, even those with a basic green plumage, have a red marking on their heads. In three-toed woodpeckers, this marking is bright yellow. Its home in mountain chains is at the highest altitudes, in zones where

coal
titmouse

crested tit

crossbill

bullfinch

only the highest conifer trees live. It rarely ventures below 5,250 feet (1,600 m). Because altitudes this high are scattered, its distribution area is split up. Also, ornithologists (scientists who study birds) do not venture into these altitudes very often to check whether the woodpeckers are actually living there.

When in search of food, the three-toed woodpecker behaves in a very unusual manner. It climbs up pine and fir trees in a spiral. Another bird that does this is the tree creeper, a small songbird with a curved beak, which looks for insects in cracks in tree bark. But the woodpecker is a more powerful bird. When it finds insects nesting in wood, it scares them out with swift, hard taps of its beak. It will then catch the insects with its sticky tongue. It can shoot out its tongue to a distance twice the length of its head. Holes made in a spiral shape in a tree trunk are a clear sign that a three-toed woodpecker has been at work.

The other woodpecker species have a greater effect on the forest. The most damaged trees will be completely stripped of bark. The bird which probably did this is the black woodpecker. This is the largest and most powerful of all the woodpeckers. It is unmistakable in appearance, being almost 20 inches (50 cm) long and black all over except for red feathers on the top of its head. The female has a smaller red area than the male. This species needs large forested areas where the treetops are not too close together. They require large old trees to make nest holes, preferably beech or fir trees. The black woodpecker finds these conditions in the Alps and in the Pyrenees. Farther north, it also lives in lowland areas. It has rarely been seen farther south than the Alps and the Pyrenees. You can always tell when the black woodpecker is around since it makes many kinds of pounding and hammering sounds and a wide variety of vocal noises. These include a loud clicklike noise which sounds like the beginning of a factory siren. It is about as loud as a siren, too. The woodpecker makes this call at all hours of the day.

The other woodpeckers are the great spotted, the middle spotted, the lesser spotted, the white-backed, the green, and the gray-headed woodpecker. They live in mountains up to a certain altitude throughout the year. This is because they do not leave the forests which are their habitat, even in lowland areas.

Small Songbirds

In a book written by Renato Perlini in 1923 called

black redstart

whitetail

rock bunting

bank swallow

Alpine Fauna, the author listed fifty-three species of songbirds nesting in the Alps. But this list is actually longer and is still being added to today. This large number of species may make it seem that the alpine area is overcrowded. But each species has a certain place, or niche, in which it lives, so there are no such problems. Also, there are fewer individual birds and fewer species as the altitude increases. This is a general rule and is true both for birds and vertebrates. The first sudden decrease in the numbers of animals occurs when the broadleaf trees come to an end. A second, even more sudden drop occurs above the uppermost tree line. As the number of animals drops and the altitude increases, the arctic features which mountain animals usually have are found.

The first typical songbird species are certain titmice. These birds live in the evergreen forest zone. They may also appear lower down, but it is in the evergreen forests that they occur in the greatest numbers. The species are the crested tit, the coal titmouse, and the willow tit. All three are very busy little birds, performing endless acrobatics to find food above and beneath branches. Sometimes they can be seen casually hanging upside down.

During the winter, these titmice form mixed flocks with other titmouse species at lower altitudes. These include the blue tit, the great tit, and the long-tailed tit. They will also gather together with other birds which can be found in flatter parts of mountain areas, such as goldcrests, the nuthatches, and sometimes tree creepers. As soon as one of these flocks arrives in the woods, the entire area will suddenly come to life. The small birds head toward various plants. Each species knows exactly where it belongs and where to find food. For example, the tree creeper searches at the trunk while the coal titmouse searches the outermost branches of trees.

The size of the flocks tends to be fairly large since these species produce many young. Some of their nests will contain ten young. Unfortunately, nine-tenths of these offspring are destined to die during the cold winter months, usually from hardship, illness, or a predator. This is nature's way of making sure that the number of individuals able to reproduce does not change from one year to the next. This means that the various species' populations will remain constant. The titmice nest in hollows and holes which may be natural or made by other animals, or by people.

Certain members of the finch family also live where

The water ouzel, or dipper, is a rather cautious bird. Its specialty is "fishing" on the bottoms of mountain streams. If it spots something interesting as it flies along its "private" stream, it will suddenly switch directions. Or sometimes, to avoid being seen, it will soar upward and fly high over the intruder. Despite its shy behavior, it is common to see this bird skimming over the water or perched on a rock getting ready for a fishing expedition.

there are conifers. The small, bright green citril finch and the redpoll build nests in small groups or colonies but only where there are coniferous trees. This same environment is used by the crossbill for reasons related to its diet. In this bird, the upper and lower parts of the bill cross at the tips. This allows the bird to pry apart pinecones in order to remove seeds, which are their only food. In fact, they will only reproduce when there is plenty of food available. They do not mate during any certain time like all the other birds. As a result, they nest any time between January and September. They are rather active birds and slightly awkward

when moving about. The males are red; the females are green. When these birds are removing seeds from pinecones, they seem like parrots which have somehow slipped out of their natural environment.

The bullfinch is another finch in the Alps which is typical of evergreen woods. In northern areas, this bird also lives in open lowland areas. Its song, which is pleasant to hear, has made the bullfinch a popular bird to keep as a pet. The song it sings is like a soft one-note flute. The male has a very bright wine-red breast, a gray back, and a white rump. The head, wings, and tail are black. Its beak is short and thick.

Outside woodlands, in open areas and especially in areas with many rocks, there are those species of thrushes which live only in mountains. At lower altitudes is the redstart. This bird likes to nest under roofs or in holes in the walls of mountain sheds. Higher up is the black redstart. This bird is like the ordinary redstart but much darker in color. It can often be seen near mountain streams. Both of these species have a bright red tail which moves up and down all the time. This type of tail movement must be of some specific use because it is also found in the rock thrush. This beautiful thrush is the size of a blackbird, with a pure orange-red breast, a bluish back and head, and a white rump. It is often seen sunning itself on exposed rocks. This is also a favorite pastime of the whitetail, which is similar but less colorful.

The members of the genus *Turdus*—the ring ouzel and the fieldfare—are found mostly in the forest, which they use for nesting. They use meadows and mountain pastures as their feeding grounds.

Rocky mountainsides give shelter to several other species. Scattered shrubs contain the nests of buntings: the yellow bunting and the rock bunting. These small, rather dull-colored birds feed mainly on grass seeds. When they catch insects, which are very nutritious, it is for feeding the young in the nest. This habit is shared by almost all the seed-eating birds. When the young have left the nest, they gather in large flocks. These flocks then fly off into lower valleys. Here, where conditions are better, they molt their covert feathers which are found at the front of the wings and tail. During molting, feathers drop off, to be replaced by a new set. Thick, warm plumage is necessary to survive the harsh winter, but feathers formed in the nest are not warm enough for the low temperatures. An average person

95

The ring ouzel lives in rocky mountain areas where there are shrubs and bushes. It is also found on the edges of forests. It leaves both these habitats when it migrates to North Africa for the winter. In the Alps, it often nests in conifers, sometimes high off the ground. It lays five to six eggs which both parents sit on for two weeks. The young are fed small invertebrates. During the autumn and winter, its diet consists mainly of berries and different types of wild fruit.

may not notice these birds, hidden in grass as they peck away at seeds. But if there are intruders, they will fly off and display a pair of white marks on the sides of their tails. These marks are their only outstanding feature.

Steep cliffs are an ideal home for a species which is always present during mountain summers. This is the sand martin or bank swallow. It is a very pretty songbird which is a true expert in the art of flying. In fact, it eats only tiny insects which it catches while flying all day long. This species forms colonies in rock walls with many holes and cavities. Sometimes there are large numbers of birds in a colony. This is also what the alpine swift does. It does not belong to the same family as the bank swallow but looks very much like a swallow and lives in a very similar way. The shape of these two birds is identical. The body is pointed; the wings are long and pointed. The color is almost the same, too. Both species have brown wings and bodies, with white undersides. The only real difference is that the alpine swift has a wide brown stripe running across its breast.

Another way to tell the two birds apart is by size. The swift is about 8 inches (20 cm) long, and the swallow only 5 inches (12 cm). Both species reach their northernmost limit in the Alps. Elsewhere they are found along the shores of the Mediterranean Sea and in the Mediterranean islands, where they nest in cliffs. These birds all leave in late September, when the first cold spell arrives. They winter in more southerly places.

The wall creeper is found in the same distribution area for the same reason. The wall creeper does not migrate like swifts and swallows, but it does nest on cliffs and rock walls. The wall creeper also finds its food in these places. It eats small insects and larvae which it finds in cracks among the small number of plants growing there. Unlike swifts and swallows, the wall creeper nests far away from other wall creepers. In fact, a single pair occupies a very large territory. This means that wherever this bird is found, its numbers are always small.

This species has adapted very well to the life it leads. Its feet are designed in such a way that the bird can cling to almost smooth walls. It has long toes equipped with sharp nails. The slender, curved beak enables it to get at small

Migration routes of the redwing, *shown above*, move from its nesting areas in central Sweden *(below left)* and southern Finland *(below right)*. These movements have been mapped by using leg rings to label the birds.

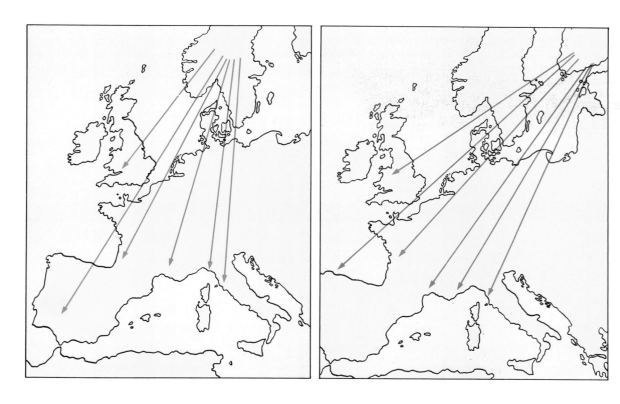

chaffinch

song thrush

tree pipit

pied
flycatcher

animals hidden in cracks. Its color is gray, like the background against which it moves. When flying, however, two bright red wings suddenly appear, which the creeper beats with a fluttering movement. This unmistakable appearance has earned the wall creeper its description as a very typical high altitude species. In fact, although it occurs at altitudes even higher than 8,200 feet (2,500 m), it is found here not because of the altitude but because of the certain habitat it requires.

The steepest slopes are also inhabited by the wren. This tiny bird is plump and lively. It weighs just 5 grams (about one fifth of an ounce). It holds its small tail straight up. It occurs from lowland areas to altitudes of almost 10,000 feet (3,000 m). The wren can be found wherever there are low shrubs and bushes which can be used for shelter.

The water ouzel, or dipper, has the same shape as the wren, with the same short, upright tail. The water ouzel offers a real surprise for beginning bird-watchers and nature lovers. It is 7 inches (18 cm) long and dark brown with a large white area under the throat. It can only be seen along mountain streams and rapids where it looks for small invertebrates to eat. It is a good swimmer and usually swims upstream. Sometimes it moves about over rocks both above the surface and under the water. To move under the water along the bed of a stream, it moves its wings as if it were flying. When it flies downstream in the air, it flies fast and low, following every twist and turn of the stream. Its nest is always built close to water. The most protected nests are built behind waterfalls.

Above the tree line, the environment is an open grassland. These grasses are mostly sedges and fescues which can stand dry conditions well. Here and there will be boulders and sometimes clumps of dwarf pine or rhododendron. Only one bird, the snowfinch, manages to live on the small food supply provided by this vegetation. It is the only seed-eating species at this altitude. All the other small birds observed feed either totally or mostly on insects. The snow finch seems quite similar to the bunting in terms of habitat and appearance. But a closer look shows it is similar to the house sparrow. Both of these birds belong to the weaverbird family.

Because of its unusual location, the snow finch deserves a detailed description. It is slightly larger than other mountain-dwelling, seed-eating birds, measuring 7 inches (18 cm). This allows it to stand the low temperatures even

A male rock thrush is banded at the ornithological station in Lomba.

Following page: Large flocks of choughs can be seen in mountains at all altitudes above 3,300 feet (1,000 m). They will also fly close to human settlements.

better. A larger body means less overall heat loss. This is because a larger body has less surface area through which to lose heat. The head is gray, the back brown, and it has a small black bib. Its underside is cream-colored. When the wings are opened, they reveal two broad white bands which contrast with the rest of the body. In the summer, the snow finch nests in cracks in rocks or beneath stones. Sometimes it may nest in structures such as mountain or cable car towers. In winter, it gathers in flocks which may contain up to two hundred birds.

The snow finch lives on mountain peaks. In the Pyrenees it is found up to the lower year-round snow line. The same is true in the Alps, the Carpathians, the Balkans, the Caucasus, and the mountains of Asia. In northern parts of Europe, there is an ecological cousin called the "snow bunting." This bird has very similar plumage and leads the same type of life. But it is found only in northern areas.

Among the insect-eating birds, the alpine accentor and rock pipit live in the same distribution area as the snow finch. They are common in alpine meadows in the moun-

tain chains of southern Eurasia. Both have a brown plumage, which is speckled and dull. The accentor is a stouter bird and has an unusual black-and-white collar. In summer, the rock pipit has a yellowish pink color on its lower parts.

Other insect-eating birds which nest in lowland areas in the north move to the mountains during the mating season. These include hedge sparrows, tree pipits, and whinchats, which sometimes venture up to altitudes of 8,200 feet (2,500 m). This group also includes the gray wagtail and white wagtail, which follow streams up to altitudes between 6,500 and 8,500 feet (2,000 to 2,600 m). But all these birds head back to the lowlands when winter comes. The alpine accentor and rock pipit also move to lower altitudes. They change their feeding habits and eat fruit and seeds. At this time, the accentor becomes very bold and will often fly into villages in search of food.

Migration Across Mountain Passes

Before winter comes, many bird species take amazing migratory trips. These migrations usually take the birds in a southwesterly direction. Because of their location, the mountain ranges of Europe separate these birds from where they spend the winter. This is why migrating birds fly toward these ranges and cross them using passes. People near a mountain pass on certain days of the year may witness hundreds of small birds flying by on their way south from the countries of northern Europe.

In scientific stations, a small metal ring called a "band" is placed around the leg of any bird caught. The band, which weighs practically nothing, lists the name of the place where the bird has been caught and an official seal followed by a number. The band, which has the same function as a car's license plates, gives the bird carrying the ring its very own identity. There are dozens of these banding stations all over Europe. Today, there are hundreds of thousands of banded birds in nature. The information they provide tells much about the body size of the different species and about the various populations of any given species, with its geographical distribution. More importantly, by catching birds in different places, a picture of their migration schedules and routes can be put together. The knowledge available today concerning these phenomena is due to the enthusiasm shown by a handful of ornithologists in banding programs.

AMPHIBIANS AND REPTILES

A list of all the amphibians and reptiles encountered in Europe's mountains would mean discussing just about all such animals that are found in Europe. For example, there are frogs, like the European frog, which lays its eggs in ponds up to altitudes of 8,000 feet (2,500 m). There are also snakes like the viper which venture readily up to the 10,000-foot (3,000 m) mark. But just a few species are limited to living only in mountains.

The Viviparous Lizard

One distinctive reptile is the viviparous lizard. It is brown with several bright stripes on its back. It measures up to 7 inches (18 cm) in length. The tail is 5 inches (12 cm) long. This reptile manages to live well in cold climates, even at altitudes of more than 10,000 feet (3,000 m). The fertilized eggs are kept in the mother's body, and the young are then born fully developed. This is the meaning of "viviparous." Another unusual adaptation of this species has to do with the way males and females divide up their periods of daytime activity. Females are more active in the early morning or late afternoon, while males move about mainly in the middle of the day. In this way, there is an even use of the available food.

The Black Salamander

The black salamander is an amphibian. It reproduces in the same way as the viviparous lizard. The mother keeps the babies in her body until they are fully developed. Unlike the previous lizard species, however, the young salamanders, usually two in number, are not enclosed in egg shells. They can move about inside the mother and feed on other undeveloped eggs. Both the black salamander and the viviparous lizard can be found in high altitude forests, especially where there are Norway spruce trees. Lizards are nevertheless more common toward the edges of these woodlands.

The Alpine Newt

This amphibian is smaller than the salamander, measuring about 4 inches (10 cm). The alpine newt depends more on water than the black salamander. It spends most of its life in small lakes and ponds at altitudes between 5,000 and 8,000 feet (1,500 to 2,500 m). It feeds mainly on invertebrates living on the bottom. During mating season, these newts become bright blue, with black-spotted yellow sides.

Opposite page: A yellow-and-black salamander, like its cousin the black salamander, has the typical shape of an amphibian. In the adult stage, it may live completely out of water, spending most of its time in holes in the ground or under old tree stumps in fairly cool, shady places. It lives especially in broadleaf woods and never reaches high altitudes. It is easy to find this creature during damp weather, early in the morning, and after rain.

GUIDE TO AREAS OF NATURAL INTEREST

Traveling through Europe's mountains in search of plant life and wildlife means leaving the car behind and walking along pathways, first through broadleaf forests, then through evergreen forests, and finally through colorful grasslands. Here there is plenty of room to admire beautiful views of mountain ridges and peaks.

Some basic equipment is needed to get the most out of mountain hiking. It should include climbing boots, woolen socks, mountaineering trousers, a waterproof parka, a backpack, sunglasses, and binoculars. A good pair of binoculars is important for a close look at nature.

The best time for a nature hike in the mountains is fairly short. It lasts from June to September, or possibly October. In late spring, it is easy to come upon areas still covered with snow or ice. So it is best to have a pair of crampons (steel spikes that are strapped on shoes), too. At any time of year, there may be a sudden storm or even a snowfall. A waterproof parka should always be kept at hand, as well as a spare woolen sweater.

There are hundreds of books about hiking on mountain paths and trails. Some trails will allow hiking for days or even weeks, stopping at refuges and cabins, or even in caves. Such a hike can be an unforgettable experience. But be sure to know your own strength and endurance. Above all, do not overestimate your own experience. A week at high altitude with seven to eight hours hiking a day over mountain paths requires that you be quite fit. Hiking off the main trails is not advisable, unless you have already experienced such conditions. Special mountaineering gear is needed, and you should be accompanied by an expert guide.

Long hikes along "easy" paths and trails are the best way of seeing plenty of plant life and animals, as well as scenery. If you take difficult routes and do not have the necessary experience, you run two risks. You will be putting yourself in danger, and you will probably not see many animals. In fact, the concentration needed for getting around in "difficult" areas makes it hard to observe the natural surroundings.

Here are a few tips. Do not forget to take food. If you go in a group, each member of your group should walk at his or her own pace. Make arrangements to meet at certain points along the route. If you rest and have something to eat, the only trace you should leave behind is, at most, a small patch of slightly-flattened grass, and nothing else.

Opposite page: A hiker approaches two male ibex in Gran Paradiso National Park (Italy) for picture taking. Hiking in the parks has strict rules and regulations in order to preserve the natural heritage. Parks are there to protect this heritage.

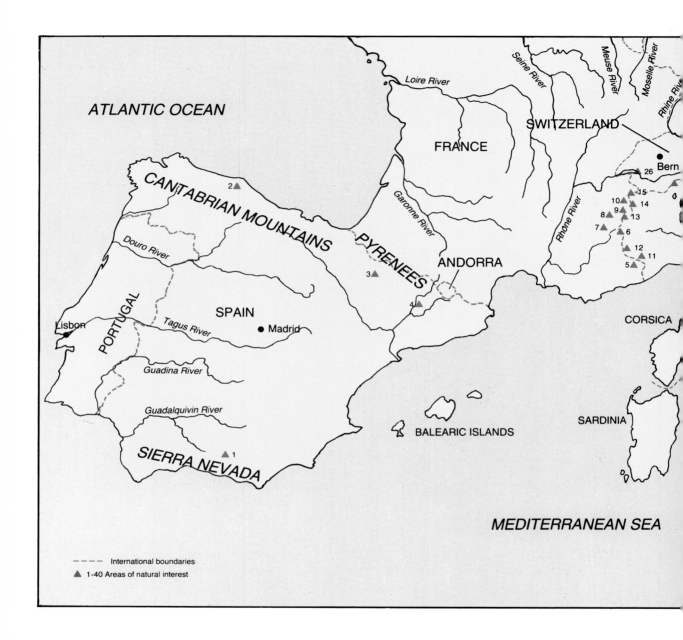

Above: The map shows only the most important of the areas currently protected in the mountain ranges of Europe.

SPAIN

Sierra Nevada (1)

The Sierra Nevada stretches for fifty-six miles (90 km) in southern Spain between the cities of Granada and Almeria. Granada is the best starting point from which to visit the Sierra Nevada, taking the road which climbs up to Mount Velera. On the lower slopes, woodlands and gardens are home to many songbirds. But the richest bird life is to be found higher up. The griffon vulture, the Egyptian vulture, and the golden eagle are quite easy to see in this area, which

106

GERMANY
Prague ●
POLAND
Danube River
CZECHOSLOVAKIA ▲ 34
RUSSIA
LIECHTENSTEIN
▲ 31
▲ 29 ▲ 30 AUSTRIA Vienna ● TATRA MOUNTAINS CARPATHIANS
▲ 32
28 ▲ ▲ 18 ▲ 33 Budapest
▲ 17 ▲ 22 HUNGARY
▲ 20 ▲ 35
▲ 19 ▲ 21 ▲ 36 ROMANIA
23 ▲
Po River ▲ 37 Bucharest ●
▲ 38
Belgrade ● BALKAN MOUNTAINS BLACK SEA
ITALY YUGOSLAVIA
▲ 24 ▲ 39 ● Sofia
APENNINES ● Rome ▲ 25 ALBANIA BULGARIA
Tirane ●
Mt. Olympus
40 ▲
GREECE TURKEY
SICILY
Athens ●

Covadonga (2)

is also one of the last areas having the lammergeyer or bearded vulture in Europe.

Covadonga National Park which is about 65 sq. mi (169 sq. km), is found in the Cordillera Cantabrica next to the provinces of Asturias and Leon. It covers the western part of the Picos de Europa mountain range. The most common species of tree here is the beech, which covers the slopes of this mountainous landscape between 2,625 and 5,000 feet (800 to 1,500 m). In the lower valleys are chestnut, durmast, and holly. Living in these woodlands are martens, wildcats, squirrels, dormice, and foxes. Large rodents called "nutrias" live in the fast-flowing streams. They eat the many trout and other fishes.

Ordesa (3)

The Ordesa National Park was established in 1918 at the same time as the Covadonga Park. Found in Aragon in the Pyrenees in Huesca province, it covers 61 sq. miles (157 sq. km). It includes not only the Ordesa Valley but also the magnificent valleys of Aisclo, Pineta, and Gargantas de Escuain. The main vegetation consists of Scotch pine, black pine, fir, and beech. Breathtaking rocky peaks provide plenty of refuge for a lot of mammals, for which the park is famous. It is home to chamois, ibex, and brown bears. In the Ordesa Valley, are the last surviving members of the Pyrenean subspecies of wild goat.

Among the birds to see are lammergeyer or bearded vultures, goshawks, peregrine falcons, griffon vultures, Egyptian vultures, choughs, golden eagles, and Bonelli's eagles.

Access to the Ordesa Valley is via Highway 170 to Torla. Then there is a narrow road inside the park. To visit the other valleys, you will need to go to Ainsa, close to the Cinca River, until you reach the start of the valleys.

Aigües Tortes y San Mauricio (4)

In the north of the province of Lérida, between the Noguera Ribagorzana and Noguera Pallaresa rivers, is the third largest mountainous national park in Spain: Aigües Tortes y San Mauricio. There are two different parts: the San Nicolau Valley and the Escrita Valley with Lake San Mauricio, and the "Els Encantats" mountain range, which soars majestically over the valley to a height of 9,013 feet (2,747 m).

The most common trees in this park are fir, Scotch pine, and, higher up, black pine. Where the woodland ends, the alpine grassland forms an important source of food for the plant-eating animals. The coniferous woods are home to capercaillies. The willow grouse can be found among the glaciers and snowfields. Among the mammals which inhabit these valleys are wild boars, chamois, ermines, dormice, and squirrels.

Access to the San Nicolau Valley is from Pont de Suert on Highway 230. The Escrita Valley can be reached from Tremp and from Sort on Highway 147.

FRANCE

Mercantour (5)

Lauzanier (6)

Escreins (7)

Vercors (8)

Ecrins (9)

The main access to the Mercantour National Park, which covers about 262 sq. miles (680 sq. km), is from Dalmas-de-Tende. Other beautiful trips can be made from St. Martin-Vésubie and Madone de Fenestre. In addition to being home to chamois and ibex, this park has several hundred mouflon (wild sheep) imported from Corsica, plus badgers, foxes, and ermine. The various species of birds include ptarmigans, rock partridges, blackcocks, golden eagles, eagle owls, and boreal owls. There is also an amazing wealth of insect life.

The Lauzanier Nature Reserve can be crossed on the GR5 path which follows the Ubayette Valley. In the reserve, it is possible to see a good variety of beautiful alpine flora and fauna.

The Escreins Nature Reserve contains mainly plant life. But there are also some interesting animals such as chamois, marmots, blackcocks, and golden eagles. The reserve can be reached by traveling from Guillestre along Highway N202 toward Vars. This road goes as far as the uninhabited village of Escreins.

Inside the reserve are a botanical garden and a laboratory of plant biology.

A good starting point from which to visit the Vercors Regional Nature Park is the small town of Villard-de-Lans. From here visitors take the road which leads to Pont-en-Royans, where the Bourne Gorge and the beautiful Choranche caves can be found.

Among the many hikes possible from Villard, the one to Col Vert should be mentioned. This takes about two hours and provides a good idea of the Vercors region. From the nearby village of Correnon, La Glacire can be reached by foot in a little more than half an hour. This is an unusual cave where, because of the low temperature, the water dripping from the roof and the walls turns into a crust of ice.

The Ecrins National Park covers 354 sq. miles (918 sq. km). It is found in the Pelvoux and Champsaur ranges at an altitude of between 2,625 and 13,462 feet (800 to 4,103 m) at the Barre des Ecrins summit. There are plenty of hikes to be made. These start out from Brianon, or from La Grave, Bourg-d'Oisans, Corps, St.Bonnet, Gap, Embrun, and Guillestre. One of the most beautiful hikes goes to the Col d'Arsine.

It takes 2½ hours on foot from Montier-les-Bains. Seen are many small plants and various birds, such as snow finches, rock pipits, and whitetails.

Another good hike leads to the Pelvoux and Selé Refuges. This takes 3½ hours by foot from Ailefroide, near Vallouise. The park headquarters are at Gap, at Rue Colonel Roux 7.

Vanoise (10)

The Vanoise National Park was set up in 1963. The main purpose was to form a refuge for the ibex on the French side of the Graian Alps. These animals were beginning to stray outside the Gran Paradiso Park too often. It is found high up between 4,100 and 12,638 feet (1,250 to 3,852 m). The animals in it are mainly high-altitude species, like ptarmigans, mountain hares, ermines, marmots, chamois, and golden eagles.

The park can be reached from the Arc and Maurienne valleys, using highways 6 and 202, or from the Isère and Tarentaise valleys, using highways 90 and 202. These roads meet at Col de l'Iseran. Several villages can be used as starting points, and there are plenty of hikes to be made. The points of interest along the 310 miles (500 km) of paths and trails are well marked with wooden signs.

ITALY

Valdieri-Entracque (11)

The Valdieri-Entracque Nature Reserve is the largest in the piedmont region. It covers some 100 sq. miles (259 sq. km). The village of Valdieri, which is 6 miles (10 km) from Borgo San Dalmazzo and 11 miles (18 km) from Cuneo, can be used as a starting point for all the hikes. From Terme di Valdieri, it is possible to reach the many refuges in the Argentera area. There are many trips to be made from Entracque. Those to Piano del Preit, Col de Fenestre, and the Mercantour National Park in France are of special interest.

The rich wildlife in this reserve includes chamois, ibex, marmots, foxes, martens, stone martens, weasels, ermines, hares, and badgers.

Argentera and Thuras (12)

The Argentera and Thuras valleys have for years formed a protected area for a rich wildlife including chamois, ibex, and eagles. The plant life is beautiful, and the landscape is still untouched despite nearby important tourist centers like Sestrière. This area covers 116 sq. miles (300 sq. km) and includes the Thuras, Troncea, and Argentera valleys, as well as the high Germanasca Valley. This valley rises up to the 10,837-foot (3,303 m) summit of Punta Ramiere.

Osiera-Rocciavr (13)

Together with Mount Rocciavrè, Mount Orsiera forms the heart of a large region untouched by roads or built-up areas of any sort. It covers about 31 sq. miles (80 sq. km) between the Susa Valley and the Chisone Valley. The mountain and woodland landscape is filled with springs, streams, and small lakes. Of particular beauty is Lake Ciardonnet at the foot of Mount Orsiera. The mammals present include marmots, chamois, hares, badgers, and foxes.

Access to the park is by the Susa Valley, from the villages of Bussoleno and San Giorgio. There are paths leading to the Gravio and Toesca refuges. Access is also possible from the Chisone Valley and Forno.

Gran Paradiso (14)

The Gran Paradiso National Park is certainly one of the richest alpine areas for wildlife. Established in 1922, it covers an area of about 270 sq. miles (700 sq. km). It is home to about three thousand ibex, five thousand chamois, and at least ten thousand marmots. It also has mountain hares, ermine, golden eagles, blackcocks, ptarmigans, rock partridges, choughs, and ravens. Among the smaller birds are coal titmice, whitetails, redpolls, linnets, snow finches, and rock pipits. One of the most unusual species is certainly the wall creeper.

Main access routes to the park are along the Valsavaranche and Cogne Valley roads. The best hikes lead to the Victor Emmanuel II Refuge, from Pont, in Valsavaranche; the Orvielles cabin, from Degioz, also in Valsavaranche; and the Vittorio Sella Refuge, from Valnontey, near Cogne. At Valnontey do not forget to visit the Paradisia Alpine Gardens, among the finest in the Alps.

Poppies bloom in the Paradisia Alpine Gardens at Valnontey (Val d'Aosta). Such "alpine gardens" are now a popular tourist attraction in most mountainous regions.

From the piedmont side, it is possible to reach the park via the Locana Valley. A road leads along the Piantonetto Valley, and another almost reaches the Nivolet Pass. From here, it is possible to reach Valsavaranche on foot.

Mont Blanc (15)

The main trips to Mont Blanc start out from Courmayeur or Chamonix. From Chamonix, it is possible to visit the Mer de Glace or "Sea of Ice" by narrow gauge train, as well as the Bossons Glacier. From the Italian side, the top of Mont Blanc can only be reached by skilled mountaineers. It is more easily reached from the French side, from Chamonix or St. Gervais. Anyone not used to hiking in mountains can

Poppies bloom in the Paradisia Alpine Gardens at Valnontey (Val d'Aosta). Such "alpine gardens" are now a popular tourist attraction in most mountainous regions.

still reach the Aiguille du Midi by taking the cable car from La Palud, in Courmayeur, or from Chamonix. A complete tour of the mountain on foot using existing high-altitude paths usually takes eight to twelve days for an average hiker. There are plenty of books and maps published about Mont Blanc by Italian and French alpine clubs. On the Italian side, a protected area has recently been established to help the populations of mountain animals. The animals here include chamois, ibex, roebucks, a few crows from Switzerland, and golden eagles.

The Veglia and Devero Alps (16)

A single regional nature park has been formed by the combined basins of the Veglia and Devero Alps. This is an area of great geological and botanical interest. There are numerous traces of ancient glaciers, such as moraines, scattered boulders, and cirque lakes.

The plant life is very rich. It includes interesting and rare species, such as unscented carnation, cinquefoil, willow herb, and edelweiss.

The wildlife is not abundant but includes chamois, marmots, ermines, and blue hares. The birds include alpine accentors, choughs, ring ouzels, ravens, blackcocks, ptarmigans, and rock partridges.

Access to the Veglia Alps is along Highway 33 from the Simplon Pass to Varzo, turning off in the direction of San Domenico. Beautiful hikes include climbing up to Lake Bianco, which takes an hour and a half; to Pian Sass Mor, in an hour and a quarter; to Streghe Lake; the Rio Cianciavero "giants' kettles"; and the Aurona Valley. The Devero Alps are reached by taking the road along the Formazza Valley to Baceno, and then turning toward Goglio.

Lake Mezzola (17)

Lake Mezzola is an offshoot of Lake Como. It is a protected area for trout, chub, perch, burbot, tench, carp, eels, and rudd. There is also a rich variety of water plants, including meadow foxtail, water chestnut, and waterlilies.

Behind Lake Mezzola is the Pian di Spagna marshland. Here herons, wild ducks of many species, grebes, and swans can be found.

At an altitude of 1,378 feet (420 m) on the western shore of the lake, stands the charming village of Albonico. In August 1983, the first ornithological station in Lombardy was set up here. It is highly equipped to study the area's permanent and migratory bird life using the latest international methods.

Stelvio (18)

Lake Tovel (19)

Puez-Odle (20)

Paneveggio (21)

The Fanes, Sennes, and Braies Dolomites (22)

The Stelvio National Park covers two regions: Lombardy and Trentino Alto Adige. It has an area of 520 sq. miles (1,350 sq. km) and includes within it the beautiful Ortles, Gran Zebru, and Cevedale mountains. Their peaks soar up to almost 13,124 feet (4,000 m). There are, in all, 103 glaciers and 42 small lakes in this park. Forests make up over one-fifth of the total area. They contain all the main alpine conifers: Norway spruce, larch, cembran pine, and dwarf pine.

The wildlife includes roebucks, deer, chamois, ibex (which were released in 1968), marmots, mountain hares, martens, ermines, badgers, squirrels, and oak dormice. More than 130 species of birds have been observed, including golden eagles, goshawks, pygmy owls, capercaillies, blackcocks, ptarmigans, hazel hens, nutcrackers, and choughs.

The best-known valleys in the Trentino area are the Monte and Mare valleys, which can be reached from Cogolo di Pejo. Also, Rabbi Valley can be reached from the Tonale highway. The Alto Adige Valleys include the Trafoi, Solda, and Martello valleys.

Lying at the foot of the Brenta Dolomites, Lake Tovel and the Tovel Valley form a nature park. It is famous for the red water caused by a single-celled alga. The lake, surrounded by thick forest, is the home of barbel, char, and minnows. The Tovel Valley is one of the last refuges of the brown bear.

The Puez-Odle Nature Park covers an area of 36 sq. miles (94 sq. km) and includes the Odle and Puez dolomite peaks. One of the loveliest parts of this region is Vallunga, which can be reached from Selva di Val Gardena. Mount Seceda is located here, where the western peaks offer a splendid geological cross section for seeing sedimentary formations.

The Paneveggio protected area consists of a huge state forest, plus the Pale di San Martino Range. The nature park covers 61 sq. miles (158 sq. km). It is the home of every mountain species of plant and animal found in the Stelvio Park and includes large numbers of deer. The forest is reached by Highway 40 between Predazzo and Paneveggio.

The central point of this large mountain park, with its highly interesting variety of plants and animals, is the famous Lake Braies. This can be reached from the Pusteria Valley.

Iseo Peat Bogs (23)

Near Provaglio d'Iseo, 3 miles (4 km) from Iseo, there is an area with beautiful peat bogs. Unfortunately, most of the bogs have dried up, despite state action taken in 1968. This action involved certain conservation rules designed to protect the fish and bird life. But the pools here are still filled with rudd, tench, carp, eels, pike, and perch. The reeds provide nesting sites for little bitterns, mallards, teal, and garganey. The marsh plant life is also interesting.

Sibilline Mountains (24)

Covering Umbria and the Marches, the Sibilline Mountains are one of the most prized natural areas in both provinces.

Covered with large beech woods and a rich plant life, these mountains are every bit a match for higher ranges like the Alps. But there is little animal life, except for a population of choughs, a couple of pairs of golden eagles, a few rock partridges, and a few ravens. Wolves are rarely seen here. They were wiped out years ago by people and have only been protected since 1970.

Abruzzi National Park (25)

The Abruzzi National Park is found in the heart of the central Apennines. It includes the mountains which link the Marsica range in Abruzzi with the Ciociaria and Mainarde mountains in Molise. It covers an area of 155 sq. miles (400 sq. km) The rich tree life includes beech woods mixed with yew, sycamore, maple, ash, rowan-tree, and holly.

There are important stands of black pine, belonging to a variety found only in this region, and only in the Camosciara and Fondillo valleys. Gentian, primrose, violet, anemone, lilies, orchids, saxifrage, buttercups, hellebore, sweet woodruff, and dentaria can be found here. Of all the flowers, however, the rarest and most famous is the lady's slipper orchid, a beautiful yellow-and-black species.

The wildlife is truly exceptional, with brown bears, Abruzzi chamois, and the Apennine wolf representing the rarest species. There are also martens, stone martens, skunks, badgers, wildcats, foxes, dormice, moles, otters, and many bird species.

Highway 83 runs through the park, passing through Pescasseroli. This village makes a good starting point for the many hikes to be made in the region.

SWITZERLAND

Pierreuse and Vanil Noir (26)

The Pierreuse and Vanil Noir reserves are rich in plants and wildlife. They are found in the northern limestone Alps not far from one another. Access is from Château-d'Oex (Vaud Canton).

Goldau landslide (27)

On September 2, 1806, a colossal landslide tumbled away from Mount Rossberg and entirely buried the township of Goldau. The huge and impressive boulders that crashed down the mountainside are still visible in a small area which is almost part of the town. In the woods that have grown up among the boulders, there is an interesting zoo with deer, fallow deer, mouflon, and other animals in semicaptivity.

Swiss National Park (28)

The Swiss National Park is one of the oldest protected areas in Europe. It is found on the eastern slopes of the Inn Valley in the Engadine district and covers an area of 66 sq. miles (170 sq. km) About one-third of the park is covered by forest, made up mostly by the Swiss mountain pine. The park is the home of four species of hoofed mammals: roebucks, deer, chamois, and ibex, which have been released there. The carnivore population includes badgers, foxes, weasels, ermines, skunks, martens, and lynx. The lynx was released into the park in 1972. The bird life includes golden eagles, capercaillies, blackcocks, ptarmigans, rock partridges, and hazel hens.

The best starting point from which to visit the park is Zernez, where the Chasa dal Parc Naziunal Svizzer can be found. One of the finest trips from Zernez leads to the Cluozza Cabin and takes three hours. Another less strenuous hike takes an hour and a half and leads to Margunet in the direction of the Forno Pass. Here, there are many large mammals.

WEST GERMANY

Allgau Alps (29)

The Bavarian side of the Allgau Alps is almost entirely occupied by a nature reserve. The main starting point to explore this protected area is Oberstdorf, in West Germany. From here a cable car takes visitors just below the Nebelhorn Peak. The edge of the reserve borders on the Tyrol and includes an area which contains the Vilstal Lakes.

Ammer Mountains (30)

From Reutte in the Tyrol, a beautiful road reaches the Deutsche Alpenstrasse in Bavaria, heading for Oberammergau. It passes through a large area of the famous Bavarian Forest. The Ammer Mountains Nature Reserve is here in the Ammergauer Alpen. On the Austrian stretch of this drive, the most interesting area is along the shores of the Plansee.

Bayerischer Alpenpark (31)	Lying between the Lofer-Bad Reichenhall-Salzburg road and the Austrian border, the Bayerischer Alpenpark includes the Königssee National Park in its southern half. The Deutsche Alpenstrasse runs through the Alpenpark.

AUSTRIA

Karwendel Mountains (32)

The very large nature reserve in the Karwendel Mountains is of great interest. It is found in the area lying between the towns of Seefeld, Jenbach, Achenpass, and Wallgau. Deer and chamois live in the reserve, and a starting herd of ibex has been released into the Pertisau area.

The center of the reserve is near Eng Mountain. It can be reached from the north by turning off the Deutsche Alpenstrasse near Vorderriss. From the Eng, there are several paths leading up to high altitude points of interest.

Furtner Teich (33)

Found near Mariahof in Styria, the Furtner Teich Nature Reserve includes the small and large Furtner Teich and a large area of reeds. This is one of the oldest bird-watching stations for migrating birds. The area is important because of its position at the Neumarkt Saddle, where migrating birds rest.

POLAND

Tatry Mountains (34)

The Tatry National Park is found in both Czechoslovakia and Poland. It includes a granite section in the Tatry Mountains themselves and a limestone section in the Belanske Hills. The highest peak is Mount Gerlach which is 8,711 ft. (2,655 m) tall and is largely covered with Norway spruce forest. The park is famous for its mammals, which include lynx, bears, foxes, marmots, and ibex. The Tatry Mountains are also rich in bird life, with golden eagles, lesser spotted eagles, black storks, tawny owls, eagle owls, and capercaillies.

In Czechoslovakia, the park center is at Tatranskà Lomnica. From here a cable car goes to the top of Lomnický Stít. In Poland, the main center is Zakopane, 56 miles (90 km) south of Krakow. The park has typically mountain features and a good network of paths.

ROMANIA

Retezat (35)

Covering 50 sq. miles (130 sq. km) at altitudes of between 1,640 and 8,200 feet (500 to 2,500 m) in the southern Carpathians, the Retezat National Park boasts large coniferous forests and various small glacial lakes, cirques, and moraines. There is a very rich wildlife which includes bears, wolves, lynx, chamois, griffon vultures, European black vultures, golden eagles, capercaillies, and others.

The park is accessible from the north. The fork for the villages of Petroseni or Osarmizegetusa is on the Deva-Orastie stretch of the Bucharest-Budapest highway. Paths lead from both these villages into the park.

YUGOSLAVIA

Triglav (36)

In the northern part of the Julian Alps, around Mount Triglav, lies Triglav National Park. The plant life is highly varied and includes the Zoys bellflower. Among the amphibians present is a form which is unique to the area, the Black Lake alpine newt. The reptile population includes Horvath's lizard and the horn-nosed viper. The large mammals include roebucks, chamois, and ibex.

Access to Triglav Park is from the direction of Bled. The road ends at the Savica Refuge, near the waterfall of the same name, after running beside Lake Bohinj.

Notranjski Šneznik (37)

Notranjski Šneznik, known as "the snowy mountain," is separated from the rest of the Julian Range. It is the last southern part of these Alps. Because of its separation, the alpine flora in the botanical reserve is very rich and special. From the top of the mountain, there is a fine view over Istria. Brown bears and wolves still live on this mountain, in the dense forest.

Plitvice Lakes (38)

The seventy-six Plitvice Lakes are scattered between the Mala Kapela and Liska Pljesevica ranges in Croatia. Found in a typically karstic area (with many sinkholes), the lakes are surrounded by unusual travertine rock formations, often covered with mosses and lichens, making this one of the most extraordinary landscapes in Europe.

The area of the national park, lying 14 miles (22 km) from Vrhovine and 112 miles (180 km) from Zagreb, is covered with huge beech woods, mixed with hornbeam, elm, and maple. Here are bears, wolves, wildcats, every species of woodpecker found in Europe, tawny owls, and others.

Durmitor (39)

Covering about 250 sq. miles (650 sq. km) around Mount Durmitor, the Durmitor National Park includes beautiful landscapes like Tara Canyon and the lake called Crno Jezero, which means "black lake." In the beech and ever-

Preceding pages: Pictured is a landscape from the shores of one of the Plitvice Lakes. These blue or greenish lakes are at different levels and connected by a series of waterfalls. They are one of the main tourist attractions in Croatia.

GREECE

Mount Olympus (40)

green forests and the mountain meadows are chamois, roebucks, deer, brown bears, capercaillies, and others.

The area is accessible from Titograd along the Niksic road for 22 miles (35 km), and then to Savnik and Zabljak.

Covering 15 sq. miles (38 sq. km) and lying between 2,460 and 9,571 feet (750 and 2,917 m), the Mount Olympus National Park is covered lower down by Mediterranean forest. Higher up there are pine and beech trees.

In addition to chamois and golden eagles, there are wild goats here. Access is possible from Lithokoron, a few miles from the Athens-Salonika freeway.

GLOSSARY

algae primitive organisms which resemble plants but do not have true roots, stems, or leaves. Algae are usually found in water or damp places.

artiodactyl any of an order of hoofed mammals having an even number of toes or cloven hoofs.

atmosphere the gaseous mass surrounding the earth. The atmosphere consists of oxygen, nitrogen, and other gases, and extends to a height of about 22,000 miles (35,000 kilometers).

basin all the land drained by a river and its branches.

broadleaf trees trees having flat rather than needlelike leaves.

caruncle an outgrowth of flesh, such as the comb and wattles of a fowl.

cirque a steep, hollow valley or excavation high on a mountainside, made by glacial erosion.

conservation the controlled use and systematic protection of natural resources, such as forests and waterways.

continent one of the principal land masses of the earth. Africa, Antarctica, Asia, Europe, North America, South America, and Australia are regarded as continents.

deciduous forests forests having trees that shed their leaves at a specific season or stage of growth.

deforestation the clearing of forests or trees. This mass removal of forests was once done for agricultural and industrial purposes. Steps are now being taken by ecologists to preserve the remaining forests and to at least partially rebuild the destroyed areas.

deformation the changing of rocks caused by folding and splitting of the earth's crust. Deformation occurs as a result of pressure deep inside the earth.

degradation the process of wearing down by erosion. All mountain chains are affected by degradation.

delta a deposit of sand and soil, usually triangular in shape. Deltas are formed at the mouth of some rivers, such as the Mississippi.

ecosystem the relationship formed by the biological environment (which includes all living things in an area) and its physical environment.

environment the circumstances or conditions of a plant or animal's surroundings. The physical and social conditions of an organism's environment influences its growth and development.

erosion natural processes such as weathering, abrasion, and corrosion, by which material is removed from the earth's surface.

extrusive rocks rocks forced out in a molten state through the earth's crust; volcanic rock.

fault a fracture or split in a rock mass, accompanied by movement of one part along the split.

fossil a remnant or trace of an organism of a past geologic age, such as a skeleton or leaf imprint, embedded in some part of the earth's crust.

geology the science dealing with the physical nature and history of the earth. Geology includes a study of the structure and development of the earth's crust, the composition of its interior, individual types of rock, and the forms of life which can be found.

geosyncline a very large, deep depression in the earth's surface containing masses of sedimentary and volcanic rocks.

habitat the areas or type of environment in which a person or other organism normally occurs. Specific environmental factors are necessary for providing a "natural" habitat for all living things.

humus a brown or black substance resulting from a partial decay of plant and animal matter.

igneous rocks rocks formed by the solidification, or hardening, of molten magma at or below the earth's surface.

intrusion the invasion of liquid magma into or between solid rock.

karst a region made of porous limestone containing deep splits and sinkholes and characterized by underground caves and streams.

lichen a primitive plant formed by the association of blue-green algae with fungi. Lichens grow in the cracks of tree bark.

lithosphere the solid, rocky part of the earth. The earth's lithosphere is split up into huge, flexible tectonic plates.

magma the molten matter under the earth's crust which is eventually released in a volcanic eruption.

metamorphic rocks rocks formed by drastic changes occurring to rock structure.

metamorphosis a change in form, shape, structure, or substance as a result of development. Rocks undergo metamorphosis when exposed to extreme pressure.

mollusk an invertebrate animal characterized by a soft, usually unsegmented body often enclosed in a shell, and having gills and a foot. Oysters, clams, and snails are mollusks.

moraine a mass of rocks, gravel, sand, and clay carried and deposited by a glacier. Moraines are simply layers or ridges of rubble which form at the sides or ends of a glacier.

organism any individual animal or plant having diverse organs and parts that function as a whole to maintain life and its activities.

orogenesis the formation of mountains through movements of the earth's crust, especially by folding and faulting.

reptile a cold-blooded vertebrate having lungs, a bony skeleton, and a body covered with scales or horny plates.

rodent any of a very large order of gnawing animals, characterized by constantly gnawing teeth adapted for chewing or nibbling.

schist any of a group of metamorphic rocks that contain layers of minerals which split easily into thin, parallel planes.

sediment matter or material that settles to the bottom of a liquid. Moving water carries sediment along its course until it reaches a stage where the current is not as strong. Sediment gathered along the way is then allowed to settle.

steppe a large plain having few trees.

tectonic plate one of several portions of the earth's crust which has resulted from geological shifting. The scientific theory of plate tectonics helps to explain how mountain chains are formed.

transpiration the giving off of moisture through the surface of leaves and other parts of the plant. The needle-shaped leaves of the conifers help to limit transpiration.

tundra a treeless area between the icecap and the tree line of arctic regions, having a permanently frozen subsoil

viviparous bearing or bringing forth living young instead of laying eggs.

INDEX

CREDITS

DRAWINGS AND MAPS, G. Vaccaro, Cologna Veneta (VR).**PHOTOGRAPHS,** B. Beaco, Verona: 13, 22-23. **F. Bergamini,** Verona: 64 **M. Bocca,** Aosta: 84, 86, 91. **L. Boitani,** Rome: 74-75. **P. Bonomi,** Verona: 6-7, 8, 36, 37, 54-55. **A. Casdia,** Brugherio (MI): 12, 14-15, 20-21, 24, 31, 34, 48, 49, 52, 57, 73, 78, 102, 104, 112-113. **L. Fornasari,** Milan: 99. **Panda Photo,** Rome: A. Boano: 32-33, 79; A. Bardi/E. Coppola: 58, 70-71; G. Cagnucci: 94-95, 96; V. Penteriani 16; A. Petretti 67; R. Ricci Curbastro 39, 44-45, 60-61. **L. Ricciarini,** Milan: J. L. Grande 26-27, 66, 76-77, 80, 82-83; O. Langini 18: L. Ricciarini cover; A. P. Rossi 87, 100-101; F. Simion 41; R. Zanette 42, 43; **S. Scolari,** Verona: 69. **F. Veronesi,** Segrate (MI): 120-121.